Evolution EXPOSED
Biology

ROGER PATTERSON

1:1
answersingenesis
Petersburg, Kentucky
United States of America

On the Cover: The cover photo shows the four actual textbooks reviewed, with yellow flags on each page containing evolutionary concepts.

Evolution Exposed: Biology—Third Ed.
Copyright © 2006, 2007, 2009 Answers in Genesis–USA. No part of this book may be used or reproduced in any manner whatsoever without the written permission from the publisher—except for brief quotations in critical reviews, articles, and research papers. For more information write: Answers in Genesis, 2800 Bullittsburg Church Rd., Petersburg, KY 41080.

Fourth printing: January 2014

ISBN: 1-60092-016-0

Cover design: Brandie Lucas & Tommy Moore
Interior layout: Diane King
Editors: Gary Vaterlaus, Stacia McKeever, Becky Stelzer, Michael Matthews
Special thanks to Ken Ham, Dr. John Morris, Dr. John Baumgardner, Dr. Georgia Purdom, and Bodie Hodge for feedback and support for the project and Dan Lietha for some of the illustrations contained in the book.

Jim Oliver's "By Faith" (p. 207) is available as a limited edition print, framed print, or canvas by calling 1-800-350-3232 to order, or visiting www.answersingenesis.org under the Museum section "Commemoratives"

All Scripture quotations are taken from the New King James Version. Copyright © 1982 by Thomas Nelson, Inc. Used by permission. All rights reserved.

Printed in China

This book is dedicated to all of those who have been deceived by evolutionary philosophies in the classrooms across the world, especially those students to whom I presented evolution as the only scientific explanation during my years as a teacher.

I would like to thank all of those who patiently modeled their faith to me through my years of doubt and disbelief and all of those who have supported me in this project. I especially thank God for the talents and courage He has provided me to speak out against the evolutionary indoctrination of our youth.

> Beware lest anyone cheat you through philosophy
> and empty deceit, according to the tradition of men,
> according to the basic principles of the world, and
> not according to Christ. —Colossians 2:8

ABOUT THE AUTHOR

Roger Patterson earned his B.S. Ed. degree in biology with a minor in chemistry from Montana State University–Billings. Before joining the curriculum development team at Answers in Genesis, he taught biology and chemistry for eight years in Wyoming's public school system and assisted the Wyoming Department of Education in developing assessments and standards for children in public schools.

TABLE OF CONTENTS

INTRODUCTION

The purpose of this book is to provide students and teachers in biology classrooms with biblical and scientific insight into the true nature of evolution as it is taught in public schools. Answers in Genesis has long suggested that students are being indoctrinated with evolutionary ideas in the public schools—this reference book provides evidence to support that claim.

After reviewing four of the most commonly used high-school biology textbooks, we found an astounding number of references to evolution. Virtually every chapter in these books contains implied or explicit references to evolutionary ideas.

This book is intended to be a reference that students can take into the classroom. Each chapter opens with a summary of the differences between the evolutionary and creationist interpretations of the chapter topic. The summary is followed by a table of the evolutionary concepts presented in the textbooks and their respective page numbers. A more thorough discussion of the topic follows the table of references. Each concept is linked to one or more articles that present a creationist interpretation of the evidence. The articles have been summarized for your convenience. Students are encouraged to read the full articles, using the provided URLs, before using the information to challenge the textbook's claims. The articles are referenced by two numbers separated by a colon. For example, article 2:5 is found in Chapter 2 and is the fifth article in the list. Complete citations for the articles are found in an index at the back of the book.

The next section contains questions that students can ask teachers concerning the ideas presented in class. Students are encouraged to ask the questions in a Christ-like manner (see the section below on Respectful Questioning). These questions are general in nature and can be modified to reflect the specific examples used in class. Following the questions is a list of books and other resources.

The indexes and tables throughout the book can be used by anyone, regardless of whether you use the textbooks.

The four textbooks cited in this book give different dates and hypotheses. When the dates disagree, the oldest date is generally given. In some cases, the hypotheses contradict one another. The statements used in the tables are intended to be generalizations, not extensive descriptions. The use of dates of millions of years and the use of common evolutionary terms is for the sake of discussion and in no way should be taken to mean that we agree with their validity.

Using the References and Companion Website

We have made every attempt to make the reference materials accessible to everyone. Whenever possible, the reference articles and chapters are available on the internet. This book also features a companion website—www.evolutionexposed.com—that can be used to link to the reference materials. The website allows you to access the most current information and will provide updates that will equip you in defending your faith. You can also use the website to access other helpful products, such as DVDs, witnessing tracts, and books.

We have chosen to use a variety of sources for the references in this book. When information from groups other than Answers in Genesis is used, articles have been selectively chosen to represent views consistent with AiG's mission and statement of faith. The websites themselves may contain material that is not necessarily endorsed by AiG.

Many organizations around the world are dedicated to upholding biblical authority and promoting that authority by addressing the creation/evolution debate. A wide variety of materials and information are available through this network of organizations. There very well may be a creation group in your local area or state. Becoming a member of one of these groups is a great way to stay connected with current issues and become equipped to engage in the culture war and advance the gospel.

Respectful Questioning & Sharing with Others

Asking questions is a proper way to challenge the ideas of teachers or textbooks, but the questions should be asked respectfully. Paul warns us in Ephesians 4:14–15:

> That we should no longer be children, tossed to and fro and carried about with every wind of doctrine, by the trickery of men, in the cunning craftiness of deceitful plotting, but, speaking the truth in love, may grow up in all things into Him who is the head—Christ.

Although evolutionary ideas are contrary to the Bible, we should speak the truth in love and show that the biblical interpretation offers a more consistent view of the history of the universe. The Bible was written by the One who created the universe and was there to see everything that happened. No one was there to observe the chemicals forming the first cell or watch as fish slowly developed legs and turned into amphibians over millions of years. Evolutionists may counter that no one was present to observe the creation of the earth—but God was there and He has recorded the highlights of those events for us in the Bible.

It is important to remember that we are ambassadors of Christ, as we are told in 2 Corinthians 5:20:

> Now then, we are ambassadors for Christ, as though God were pleading through us: we implore you on Christ's behalf, be reconciled to God.

As an ambassador in your school, you should act in a manner that reflects Christ. Others will be judging Christ based on the way that you present yourself.

When asking questions, wait for an appropriate opportunity and ask the question with a respectful tone. It would be a good idea to research the question in advance. If you know what the teacher will be discussing or if something comes up in a homework assignment, research the concept and develop an explanation that you could share with the class if the opportunity arises. It is also helpful to anticipate the teacher's answer (using the information from the articles as a guide). Play out the scenario in your mind or with a friend, and try to think of follow-up questions. Have the resource information available to share with anyone who is interested.

If the teacher wants to do further research before giving a response, you can offer a resource. If the teacher responds by saying scientists don't have the answer yet, you may want to question the validity of any other idea based on those claims. For example, "If we don't know the conditions on the early earth, how can we be sure about how cells first formed?"

Do not be surprised if the teacher responds, "That is a religious idea, and it can't be used in science." Secular science allows only natural explanations. Just because science does not allow supernatural explanations doesn't mean that supernatural explanations are not correct. This is especially true in respect to the origin of life and the historical processes that produced the world we see today. Remember, naturalistic science starts with the assumption that the Bible is not true, and creation science starts with the assumption that the Bible is true. Starting with different assumptions leads to different conclusions in almost every case. Ultimately, it takes just as much faith—if not more—to believe that only matter and natural laws can explain the universe.

The fact that the scientific community denies the supernatural does not mean that all scientists are atheists—many claim to be Christians or have other religious beliefs. Keeping that in mind, focus on ideas, not individuals. These people are not unintelligent; they simply arrive at different conclusions by using different assumptions.

If you have Christian allies in your class, it may be helpful to take turns asking questions. Also consider studying the issues together and praying for one another.

The questions provided at the end of each chapter are intended to be a starting point. Turn general questions into specific questions by incorporating examples or specific information presented by your teacher. Adapt questions to the unique situations you encounter in your classroom.

It may be difficult to share your ideas and challenge the ideas of scientists, but remember that you are not alone—God is always with you. Say a prayer and ask for courage to stand up for the truth. There is no guarantee that you will not be ridiculed, although no teacher should ridicule a student for thinking a certain way. 1 Peter 3:13–14 promises:

> And who is he who will harm you if you become followers of what is good? But even if you should suffer for righteousness' sake, you are blessed. "And do not be afraid of their threats, nor be troubled."

Peter continues with a challenge in verses 15–16:

> But sanctify the Lord God in your hearts, and always be ready to give a defense to everyone who asks you a reason for the hope that is in you, with meekness and fear; having a good conscience, that when they defame you as evildoers, those who revile your good conduct in Christ may be ashamed.

This passage tells us that we need to set apart Christ in our hearts, study to be prepared to give an answer, and speak the truth with gentleness and respect. We are in a battle, and the stakes are high. Even if a classmate or teacher does not come to Christ, you may be planting seeds that will sprout some day.

It should encourage you to know that a wealth of information is available from many sources to help you defend your faith. Below is a list of books which contain the type of information that will be helpful. These books include secular and creation scientists who challenge the idea of Darwinian evolution from both scientific and religious perspectives. There is also a huge collection of articles, some of which are summarized in the following chapters, available at www.answersingenesis.org. New articles are posted daily; so keep checking the website for the most current information regarding the creation/evolution controversy. Magazines and newsletters are another source of current information available from AiG. Many DVDs and witnessing tracts are available for you to share. The most effective changes start at the grassroots level, and you can be a powerful tool within the public school system to defend the authority of the Bible from the very first verse.

It is important that students realize they have more rights in the classroom than they might think. Whenever assignments are given, the student has the right to express his thoughts and beliefs through those assignments. For example, a report on a famous scientist might include how that scientist's faith in God or belief in the Bible influenced his career or research. Religious topics may be used whenever students are allowed to determine the content of the essay, homework, artwork, and so on. For more information on student rights in public schools visit www.answersingenesis.org/go/student-rights.

When answering questions from the textbook or teacher, students are often expected to provide answers that assume evolutionary ideas are true. In such cases, the student may want to preface the question with a disclaimer. The disclaimer might say, "According to the textbook ..." or "As the idea was presented in class ... ." This will communicate to the teacher that the student has learned the concepts presented in the class but that she does not necessarily agree with them. When appropriate, the student may also consider adding her personal beliefs or the biblical interpretation after she has answered the question from an evolutionary perspective. This approach will allow her to meet the academic requirements of the classroom setting and also express her belief that the interpretation presented by the textbook or curriculum is false.

Textbooks Reviewed

To develop this resource, four of the most popular high-school biology textbooks were chosen. The publisher and page number are provided for photos, figures, or tables (e.g., Glencoe 327). The full citations for the textbooks are listed below.

Biggs, A. et al., *Biology: The Dynamics of Life* (Florida Edition), Glencoe/McGraw Hill, New York, 2006.

This text will be referred to as Glencoe throughout this book.

Campbell, N., B. Williamson, and R. Heyden, *Biology: Exploring Life* (Florida Teacher's Edition), Pearson Prentice Hall, Upper Saddle River, New Jersey, 2006.

This text will be referred to as PH-Campbell throughout this book.

Johnson, G. and P. Raven, *Biology* (Teacher's Edition), Holt, Rinehart, and Winston, Austin, Texas, 2006.

> This text will be referred to as Holt throughout this book.

Miller, K. R. and J. Levine, *Biology* (Teacher's Edition), Pearson Prentice Hall, Upper Saddle River, New Jersey, 2006.

> This text will be referred to as PH-Miller throughout this book.

Tools for Digging Deeper

The New Answers Book 1 by Ham et al., Master Books, 2006.

> This book addresses 27 of the most common questions that creationists are asked and provides answers from a biblical perspective.

The New Answers Book 2 by Ham et al., Master Books, 2008.

> More than 30 additional questions are answered from a biblical perspective in this sequel to *The New Answers Book 1*.

The Biblical Basis for Modern Science by Henry Morris (semi-technical), Master Books, 2002.

> A comprehensive resource for the serious student of creation. Gives in-depth information on the creation/evolution issue in biology, geology, astronomy, the history of the nations, etc.

The Biotic Message by Walter ReMine (technical), Saint Paul Science, 1993.

> This book provides an exhaustive and technical treatment of information in biological systems.

Body by Design by Alan Gillen, Master Books, 2001.

> *Body by Design* defines the basic anatomy and physiology in each of 11 body systems from a creationist viewpoint.

Every chapter examines different organs and structures giving evidence for design. Students are challenged to think through the evidence—the facts as we know them today—and to consider the statistical likelihood of molecules-to-man evolution. The end result is an effective, interwoven presentation of anatomy, physiology, and creation.

Bones of Contention by Marvin Lubenow (semi-technical), Baker Books, 2004.

Professor Lubenow examines the fossil evidence for human evolution and exposes the philosophical and scientific untruths. Each of the alleged ancestors is examined and shown to be an evolutionary farce. The myth of human evolution is thoroughly dismantled in this book.

Buried Alive by Jack Cuozzo, Master Books, 1998.

Discover the startling truth about Neanderthal Man from the original research of Jack Cuozzo.

Creation: Facts of Life by Gary Parker, Master Books, 2006.

In *Creation: Facts of Life*, Dr. Parker respectfully describes the evidences he once used to preach evolution, but then he explains how the rest of the evidence points away from evolution and toward a perfect world created by God, ruined by man, restored to new life in Christ. This classic has been updated and expanded into a powerful and layman-friendly format, filled with many of the latest findings in science.

Creation Scientists Answer Their Critics by Duane Gish, Institute for Creation Research, 1993.

Dr. Gish is the world's foremost debater on creation/evolution and has debated many famous evolutionists. In this extensive work, Gish answers his critics, showing that he can substantiate all the facts given during his debates and, more powerfully, refutes the evolutionist position.

Darwin on Trial by Phillip Johnson, InterVarsity Press, 1993.

> Professor Johnson uses his incisive legal mind to demonstrate that Darwinian evolution is based not on fact, but on faith. Johnson examines the evidence used to support evolution and its naturalistic philosophy, and he declares a mistrial.

Darwin's Black Box by Michael Behe (semi-technical), Free Press, 1996.

> Biochemistry professor Michael Behe uses the concept of irreducible complexity to demonstrate how Darwinian evolution fails to provide a mechanism for building systems that work as intact units. Behe does not endorse a young earth, but his critique of evolutionary theory from within the scientific establishment demonstrates the shaky ground that the philosophy is based on.

Darwin's Enigma by Luther Sutherland (technical), Master Books, 1998.

> This powerful argument for intelligent design contains some of the most compelling data available by focusing on the very real shortcomings of the fossil record in supporting evolution. The author shows that there are truly more problems than solutions.

Evolution: A Theory in Crisis by Michael Denton, Adler & Adler, 1986.

> This book by a noncreationist is hard-hitting, factual, and objective. It does not argue in favor of creation, but is a clear, balanced, responsible, and scientifically accurate account of the ever-growing crisis in evolutionary circles.

Evolution: The Fossils Still Say No by Duane Gish, Master Books, 1995.

> The most compelling critique available anywhere of the supposedly key argument for evolution: the fossil record. Dr. Gish documents, from the writings of evolutionists, the complete absence of true evolutionary transitional forms.

The Fossil Book by Gary Parker, Master Books, 2006.

> This book uncovers the exciting story of fossils—how they formed, where they are found, and how to build your own collection—all from a creationist's perspective. Fascinating, informative, and filled with color photos and illustrations

Frozen in Time by Michael Oard, Master Books, 2004.

> Meteorologist Michael Oard gives plausible explanations of the seemingly unsolvable mysteries about the Ice Age and the woolly mammoths. Many other related topics are explained, including super floods, ice cores, man in the Ice Age, and the number of ice ages.

Genetic Entropy and the Mystery of the Genome by John Sanford (semi-technical), Ivan Press, 2005.

> Geneticist Dr. John Sanford examines the validity of evolution's primary axiom—that man is merely the result of random mutations plus natural selection. This revolutionary book details compelling new genetic evidence that the human genome is deteriorating and has always been deteriorating due to accumulations of mutations. The more scientists discover about the human genome, the less plausible Darwinism is. Sanford systematically lays out the scientific case against mutations resulting in the origin of species.

The Geology Book by John Morris, Master Books, 2000.

> Dr. Morris explains the formation and study of rocks in a clear, understandable way. The layers of rock were supposedly laid down over the billions of years of earth's history. Morris demonstrates that the rocks tell the story of creation and the catastrophe of a global Flood only a few thousand years ago.

If Animals Could Talk by Werner Gitt, Master Books, 2006.

> Told from each animal's perspective, this fascinating description of incredible design features a wide range of

animals, which all logically point to a loving Creator. A great tool for witnessing, writing projects, or debates.

In Six Days by John Ashton (semi-technical), Master Books, 2001.

This collection of essays from 50 respected scientists from many scientific fields demonstrates the false assumption that a commitment to evolution and naturalism is necessary to practice science. Each of these active scientists shares how faith in a literal interpretation of Scripture and scientific pursuits reinforce one another.

In the Beginning Was Information by Werner Gitt (semi-technical), Master Books, 2006.

This book presents what may well be the most devastating scientific argument against the idea that life could form by natural processes. The science of information is explained in detail, with many striking examples to clarify fundamental questions, such as: What are the laws of information? How did language develop? Is artificial intelligence possible?

The Lie: Evolution by Ken Ham, Master Books, 1998.

Ken Ham is best known for his message on the relevance of creation and the importance of Genesis. Humorous and easy-to-read, this book powerfully equips Christians to defend the book of Genesis and opens eyes to the harmful effects of evolution on today's society.

Not by Chance by Lee Spetner (technical), Judaica Press, 1997.

Dr. Spetner's book aims a death-blow at the heart of the whole neo-Darwinian story. The crucial battleground in the war over origins has always been the origin of information. Spetner is a noncreationist who shows that time and chance cannot produce new (more) genetic information. This book is a must for everyone who desires to defend the Bible in this increasingly "educated" society.

On the Seventh Day by John Ashton (semi-technical), Master Books, 2002.

This sequel to *In Six Days* presents essays by over 40 scientists with PhDs who explore the links between science and faith, and what that means not only to individuals but also to the entire planet.

01

Even if all the data point to an intelligent designer, such an hypothesis is excluded from science because it is not naturalistic.

—Dr. Scott Todd, Kansas State University,
Nature **401**(6752):423, Sept. 30,1999

What You Will Learn

Many people do not realize that science was actually developed in Christian Europe by men who assumed that God created an orderly universe. If the universe is a product of random chance or a group of gods that interfere in the universe, there is really no reason to expect order in nature. Many of the founders of the principle scientific fields, such as Bacon, Galileo, Kepler, and Newton, were believers in a recently created earth. The idea that science cannot accept a creationist perspective is a denial of scientific history.

To help us understand that science has practical limits, it is useful to divide science into two different areas: operational science and historical (origins) science. Operational science deals with testing and verifying ideas in the present and leads to the production of useful products like computers, cars, and satellites. Historical (origins) science involves interpreting evidence from the past and includes the models of evolution and special creation. Recognizing that everyone has presuppositions that shape the way they interpret the evidence is an important step in realizing that historical science is not equal to operational science. Because no one was there to witness the past (except God), we must interpret it based on a set of starting assumptions. Creationists and evolutionists have the same evidence; they just interpret it within a different framework. Evolution denies the role of God in the universe, and creation accepts His eyewitness account—the Bible—as the foundation for arriving at a correct understanding of the universe.

What Your Textbook Says about Science

Evolutionary Concept	Glencoe	PH-Campbell	PH-Miller	Holt	Articles
It is not necessary to distinguish between historical and operational science.	11–23, 1060–1061	19, 299	3–14	14–20	1:1, 1:2, 3:1
Observability, testability, repeatability, and falsifiability are the hallmarks of the scientific method.	11–23	27, 37–38, 305	10, 14, 369, T537	19	1:1, 1:2, 1:3
There are some questions science cannot answer.	21–22	38	5–6	—	1:1, 1:3
Questions about behavior can be answered by asking "why" questions.	—	51, 54	T870	824	1:1, 1:3
Evolution was not observed, but we can still understand how it happened.	396–397	51, 54	410	—	1:2, 1:3, 3:4
Biblical creation is religion, and evolution is science.	—	—	3	277	1:1, 1:2, 1:3

Note: Page numbers preceded by "T" indicate items from the teacher notes found in the margins of the Teacher's Edition.

What We Really Know about Science

In its original form *science* simply meant "knowledge." When someone says today that they work in the field of science, a different picture often comes to mind. Science, in the view of an outspoken part of the scientific community, is the systematic method of gaining knowledge about the universe by allowing only naturalistic or materialistic explanations and causes. The quote on page 19 reflects this attitude. Science in this sense automatically rules out God and the possibility that He created the universe because supernatural claims, it is asserted, cannot be tested and repeated. If an idea is not testable, repeatable, observable, and falsifiable, it is not considered scientific. The denial of supernatural events limits the depth of understanding that science can have and the types of questions science can ask. We may define naturalism and materialism as:

Naturalism: a belief denying that an event or object has a supernatural significance; specifically, the doctrine that scientific laws are adequate to account for all phenomena.

Materialism: a belief claiming that physical matter is the only or fundamental reality and that all organisms, processes, and phenomena can be explained as manifestations or interactions of matter.

The problem with the above definition of science is that, even though naturalistic science claims to be neutral and unbiased, it starts with a bias. The quote from Dr. Todd on page 19 demonstrates that bias: only matter and energy exist and all explanations and causes must be directly related to the laws that matter and energy follow. Even if the amazingly intricate structure of flagella in bacteria appears so complex that it must have a designer, naturalistic science cannot accept that idea because this idea falls outside the realm of naturalism/materialism. Many scientists have claimed that allowing supernatural explanations into our understanding of the universe would cause us to stop looking for answers and just declare, "God wanted to do it that way." This is, of course, false.

The ability to study the world around us is only reasonable because there is a Lawgiver who established the laws of nature. Most people do not realize that modern science was founded by men who believed that nature can be studied because it follows the laws given to it by the Lawgiver. Johannes Kepler, one of the founders of astronomy, said that science was "thinking God's thoughts after Him." Many founders of scientific disciplines, such as Bacon, Newton, Kepler, Galileo, Pascal, Boyle, Dalton, Linnaeus, Mendel, Maxwell, and Kelvin were Bible-believing Christians. As a matter of fact, the most discerning historians and philosophers of science have recognized that the very existence of modern science had its origins in a culture at least nominally committed to a biblical worldview. (See www.answersingenesis.org/go/bios.)

What, then, should Christians think of science? Science has been hijacked by those with a materialistic worldview and exalted as the ultimate means of obtaining knowledge about the world. Proverbs tells us that the fear of God, not science, is the beginning of knowledge. In a biblical worldview, scientific observations are interpreted in light of the truth that is found in the Bible. If conclusions contradict the truth revealed in Scripture, the conclusions are rejected. The same thing happens in naturalistic science. Any conclusion that does not have a naturalistic explanation is rejected.

The words *creation* and *evolution* can be used in many different ways. Evolution will be used in this book to describe the naturalistic process that is alleged to have turned molecules into man over billions of years. As *creation* is used throughout this book, it is intended to describe the supernatural acts of God who created the universe and everything in it in six, approximately 24-hour days, about 6,000 years ago. This perspective is often referred to as young-earth creationism. The true history of the universe is revealed to us from God's eyewitness perspective in the Bible. This history can be summarized as the 7 C's of history: Creation of the universe, Corruption of the universe as a result of man's sin, the judgment of mankind in the Catastrophe of Noah's Flood, Confusion of languages at Babel, Christ coming to earth to live a righteous life and then to pay for our sins on the Cross, and the future Consummation when God creates the New Heaven and New Earth. This history serves as a foundation for interpreting evidence in the biblical creationist's worldview.

Making a distinction between two types of scientific study helps us to understand the limitations of naturalistic presuppositions in science:

The examples of science used in the textbooks show only operational (observational) science. This type of science, which makes observations and repeated experiments in the present, allows us to produce technology that benefits mankind. Evolution does not fit within the definition of operational science and should be classified as historical (origins) science.

Operational (Observational) Science: a systematic approach to understanding that uses observable, testable, repeatable, and falsifiable experimentation to understand how nature commonly behaves.

Operational science is the type of science that allows us to understand how DNA codes for proteins in cells. It is the type of science that has allowed us to cure and treat diseases, put a man on the moon, build satellites and telescopes, and make products that are useful to humans. Biblical creationists believe that God has created a universe that uses a set of natural laws that operate consistently in the universe. Understanding how those laws operate is the basis for scientific thinking.

Some events defy natural laws. Christians refer to these things as miracles, but naturalistic science must find a way to explain these occurrences naturally. This approach rejects miracles in the Bible because they cannot be explained using natural laws. Such scientists occasionally try to explain the miracles in the Bible as natural phenomena, but this ultimately undermines the authority of God and His Word.

Historical (Origins) Science: interpreting evidence from past events based on a presupposed philosophical point of view.

The past is not directly observable, testable, repeatable, or falsifiable; so interpretations of past events present greater challenges than interpretations involving operational science. Neither creation nor evolution is directly observable, testable, repeatable, or falsifiable. Each is based on certain philosophical assumptions about how the earth began. Naturalistic evolution assumes that there was no God, and biblical creation assumes that there was a God who created everything in the universe. Starting from two opposite pre-suppositions and looking at the same evidence, the explanations of the history of the universe are very different. The argument is not over the evidence—the evidence is the same—it is over the way the evidence should be interpreted.

Evolutionists often claim that people misuse the word "theory" when discussing science and don't make a distinction between a scientific theory and the common use of the word "theory." You may say, "I have a theory about why Mr. Jones' hair looks funny" but that theory has never been compared to a broad set of observations. This is not the sense of a theory in science.

In light of this, few would argue that there are different types of theories. So it would be good to refine this term further to avoid any baiting and switching of the word "theory." Just as it was valuable to distinguish between operational and historical science, it would be good to do the same with operational and historical theories. A scientific operational theory is:

Operational Theory: an explanation of a set of facts based on a broad set of repeatable and testable observations that is generally accepted within a group of scientists.

That evolution has been elevated to the status of an operational theory (and "fact" in the opinion of some) is not due to the strength of the evidence, but in spite of it. Because evolutionary ideas are interpretations of past events, they are not as well-founded as testable scientific theories like Einstein's Theory of Relativity or Newton's Theory of Gravity. These theories offer predictable models and the ability to conduct experiments to determine their validity in different circumstances. Molecules-to-man evolution does not offer this opportunity because these events happened in the past. Therefore, evolution is not an operational theory. For these reasons evolution could be considered an historical theory, along with creation models and other origins theories.

Historical Theory: an explanation of past events based on the interpretation of evidence that is available in the present.

Evolution fits this definition of theory, but it relies on the

GOD'S WORD IS TRUTH

MAN DECIDES TRUTH

It is important to recognize that people's presuppositions influence the way they interpret evidence. Evolution is based on a reasoning process that rejects God. Creation starts from the authority of God's Word. Your presuppositions are like a pair of glasses that you wear to look at the world around you.

assumption of naturalism. In the naturalistic scientific community, evolution has become a theory that is assumed to be an established fact and not an explanation. Evolution is the prevailing paradigm, and most scientists have stopped questioning the underlying assumptions that the theory is based upon. Creationists develop theories, too, in light of biblical truth, but they are not as widely accepted by scientists. All interpretations (theories) of the past are based on assumptions and cannot be equated with facts that are observable in the present. This holds true for creationist or evolutionist theories. (See article 1:3 on page 29 for more on this topic.)

Evolution also relies heavily on the assumption of uniformitarianism—a belief that the present is the key to the past. According to uniformitarians, the processes in the universe have been occurring at a relatively constant rate. One of these processes is the rate of rock formation and erosion. If rocks form or erode at a certain rate in the present, uniformitarians believe that they must have always formed or eroded at nearly the same rate. This assumption is accepted even though there are no observations of the rate of erosion from the distant past and there is no way to empirically test the erosion rate of the past. However, the Bible makes it very clear that some events of the past were radically different from those we commonly observe today. Noah's Flood, for example, would have devastated the face of the earth and created a landscape of billions of dead things buried in layers of rock, which is exactly what we see.

Just as evolutionists weren't there to see evolution happen over several billion years, neither were creationists there to see the events of the six days of creation. The difference is that creationists have the Creator's eyewitness account of the events of creation, while evolutionists must create a story to explain origins without the supernatural. Just because many scientists believe the story does not make the story true. Believing the Bible and the information that has been revealed to us by our Creator gives us a foundation for thinking—including our thinking about science. Good operational science can provide us with answers to many questions about the world around us and how it operates, but it cannot answer the questions of where we came from and why we are here. Those questions are outside the scope of operational science. But we are not left without an answer. God has given us the answers to those questions in His Word, the Bible.

Reference Articles

1:1 The nature of science and of theories on origins, Gish, www.icr.org/article/391

> Scientific theories must be testable and capable of being proven false. Neither evolution nor biblical creation qualifies as a scientific theory in this sense, because each deals with historical events that cannot be repeated. Both evolution and creation are based on unobserved assumptions about past events. It is inconsistent to say that evolution qualifies as a scientific theory while creation does not. Both have scientific character by attempting to correlate scientific data within a certain framework (model).
>
> No theory of origins can avoid using philosophical statements as a foundation. Creationists use a supernatural act by an Intelligent Designer to explain the origin of the

Making observations about living organisms can increase understanding about many aspects of biology. But it is important to recognize the limitations when you cross into historical science.

universe and the life we see on earth. Evolutionists do not allow any supernatural explanation as a foundation but insist that only natural laws and processes can be used as explanations. Both are worldviews used to interpret the data. The data is the same; the interpretations arrive at different conclusions based on the starting assumptions. Allowing only evolutionary teaching in public schools promotes an atheistic worldview, just as much as teaching only creation would promote a theistic worldview. Students are indoctrinated to believe they are meaningless products of evolution and that no God exists to whom they are accountable.

Life on earth was either created or it developed in some progressive manner; there are no other alternatives. While there are many versions of both creation and evolution, both cannot be true.

1:2 Feedback: A "more glorious" means for creation? Hodge, www.answersingenesis.org/go/glorious

Accepting that God created the universe in the way that He said He did is a common stumbling block for many who want to accept the interpretation promoted by evolutionary scientists. There are many reasons why the God of the Bible would not have used evolution and the big bang to create the universe. Those who hold to this position are putting man's fallible interpretation of scientific data into the text of Genesis.

Accepting the big bang or evolution as factual accounts of the origin of life and the universe is not scientific. They are interpretations of facts. The assumptions that underlie the interpretations are based on the idea that man can determine truth independent of God. Operational science is based on repeatable observations and falsifiable statements while historical science is based on interpreting data that cannot be repeated. Operational science leads to computers and space shuttles as products of repeatable processes. Historical science leads to shifting interpretations that are not reliable.

The only way to arrive at a true interpretation is to start with true assumptions. Since the Bible is the eyewitness account of the Creator of the universe, it is the best starting point for interpreting past events.

1:3 Creation: Where's the proof? Ham, www.answersingenesis. org/go/proof

All scientists, creationist or evolutionist, have the same evidence; the difference is the presuppositions that are used to interpret that evidence. All reasoning is based on presuppositions. Biblical creationists start with the assumption that the Bible provides an accurate eyewitness history of the universe as a basis for scientific thought. Evolutionists begin with the presupposition that only natural laws can be used to explain the facts. Facts exist in the present, and our interpretations are an attempt to connect the past to the present. The evolutionists must assume everything about the past, while biblical creationists have the Bible as a "time machine" that can provide valuable insight into the past.

If someone expects you to argue that the Bible or creation is true without using the Bible as evidence, they are stacking the deck in their favor. They are insisting that facts are neutral and that truth can be determined independent of God. Facts are always interpreted, and the Word of God

It is not true to say that there is different evidence for creation and evolution. Everyone has the same evidence—it is just interpreted in different ways.

is absolutely trustworthy. Demonstrating how the Bible can be used to effectively explain a fact, like the presence of fossils, demonstrates that it is valid as a filter for interpreting facts. Many people do not realize how their presuppositions impact their thinking. Exposing a person's presuppositions will help them to see how they filter the facts, and then challenging the origin of those presuppositions will force them to evaluate their stance.

If science depends on naturalistic explanations, it must accept that our thoughts are simply the products of chemical reactions that evolved from random chance. How can you ultimately rely on randomness to evolve the correct way of thinking? If there is no God, ultimately, philosophically, how can one talk about reality? How can one even rationally believe that there is such a thing as truth, let alone decide what it is?

Questions to Consider

1. Do all scientists believe in naturalistic evolution? Why or why not?

2. There are two contenders for the history of life on earth: some form of naturalism (evolution) or supernatural creation. Are there really any alternatives to some form of naturalistic evolution in science if science is restricted to naturalism?

3. Since evolution and creation are both based on religious beliefs, why should one be taught in public schools and not the other?

4. Should there be a distinction between experimental (operational) science and historical science?

5. Since a naturalistic approach to science can only refer to materialistic explanations, how can naturalists use logic if logic is not a material part of the universe?

6. Is it necessary for science to allow only naturalism?

7. Would all scientific thought and advancement end if supernatural creation was accepted as a possible model for how the universe and life on earth began?

8. Why is supernatural creation considered to be a "science stopper" and not a "science starter," considering that most of the founding fathers of science believed in the Bible and a supernatural creation event?

9. If an all-knowing Creator God exists, wouldn't it be logical to say that He knows about the scientific laws He created? Why not use what He says as a foundation for scientific thinking?

Tools for Digging Deeper

(see a complete list in the Introduction)

The Biblical Basis for Modern Science by Henry Morris

Creation: Facts of Life by Gary Parker

Creation Scientists Answer Their Critics by Duane Gish

Darwin on Trial by Phillip Johnson

Darwin's Black Box by Michael Behe

In Six Days by John Ashton

Men of Science, Men of God by Henry Morris

On the Seventh Day by John Ashton

www.answersingenesis.org/go/science

02

Then God said, "Let the earth bring forth grass, the herb that yields seed, and the fruit tree that yields fruit according to its kind, whose seed is in itself, on the earth"; and it was so. And the earth brought forth grass, the herb that yields seed according to its kind, and the tree that yields fruit, whose seed is in itself according to its kind. And God saw that it was good.

—Genesis 1:11–12

What You Will Learn

Classification systems are used to help us organize and study living things. There are many different ways to group living things depending on the presuppositions that you start with. Evolutionists believe that all living things descended from a single common ancestor. Because they have this presupposition, they use the differences in physical traits, DNA, and protein sequences to determine relationships among different kinds of animals and plants. This assumption of a common ancestor has forced evolutionists to reorganize many of the original classifications of animals. Dinosaurs are now believed to be the ancestors of birds. Some have even suggested reclassifying birds as reptiles since the molecular evidence is interpreted to support this claim. The classification of the apes, among which evolutionists include humans, has changed to reflect the evolutionary view that humans are just intelligent apes. Some have even gone so far as to suggest that chimpanzees be included in the human genus *Homo*.

The Bible tells us that man was created in the image of God, and therefore man should not be classified as an ape. Creationists, starting from the truth found in the Bible, classify living things into distinct "kinds" and recognize the amazing genetic variety found within each kind. The field of baraminology involves studying the classification of living things through the biblical concept of the created kinds. The molecular evidence of proteins and DNA can be used to understand relationships within the created kinds, but it can't be used to understand how one kind changed into another, because that type of change has never occurred. Evolutionists will not arrive at an accurate understanding of the relationships of living things because their starting assumptions do not reflect the absolute truth available in God's Word.

What Your Textbook Says about Classifying Life

Evolutionary Concept	Glencoe	PH-Campbell	PH-Miller	Holt	Articles
Linnaeus develops a system for classification.	444	341	448–449	300	2:1
Classification is based on evolutionary relationships and physical traits.	442	T7, 341	452–453, 457	T298	2:2
Classification uses cladograms and phylogenetic trees to interpret and describe evolutionary relationships.	445, 452	345–348, T345	453, 458, T458	310	2:3, 2:4
Homologous and analogous structures are used to determine evolutionary relationships.	444	—	384, T453	305, 594	3:6, 3:7, 3:29
Dinosaurs are the ancestors of modern birds. Birds are actually closely related to alligators.	445, 452–453	345–348, T346, T558, T561, 564, 568	432, 799, 807, T807	307–309, 727, T787	2:5, 2:6, 2:7, 3:35
All life on earth came from a single common ancestor.	454–455	—	382, T382–T383, T385, 410, T418, 457, 460–461	413	3:6, 3:7, 3:8, 3:13, 3:19
Evolutionary relationships can be determined by comparing DNA and amino acid sequences. Evolutionary time can be measured with molecular clocks.	462	T303, 341, 343, T343–T344	451, 454, T454, 455, T455	220, 232, 413, 602, 737	2:8, 3:6, 3:29

Note: Page numbers preceded by "T" indicate items from the teacher notes found in the margins of the Teacher's Edition.

What We Really Know about Classifying Life

Genesis records that God created the animals and plants according to their kind. Genesis explains that God created specific kinds of animals. These kinds were able to breed and reproduce more of the same kind with a great variety of traits. It is not absolutely clear what the boundaries of the original kinds were, but it is clear from Genesis that the different animals and plants did not evolve from one another. The creation of life on earth was certainly a miraculous event that man will never be able to fully understand—it must be accepted by faith. However, it requires just as much—if not more—faith to accept the evolutionary story of the beginning of life and the first cell from lifeless matter.

The current system of classification is based on the pioneering work of the creation scientist Carolus Linnaeus. Linnaeus developed a classification system that was based on physical characteristics. Linnaeus is credited with popularizing the use of hierarchies and binomial nomenclature—the two-name system used for names in science today. Linnaeus called man *Homo diurnis* (man of the day) and grouped him in the primate group based on physical traits. Today, humans are called *Homo sapiens* (wise man). Classifying humans based on physical traits alone does not reflect the biblical idea of being created in the image of God. While it is true that humans share the physical traits attributed to mammals, humans have a spirit that distinguishes them from animals. Despite the fact that we share many traits with the primates, humans are not simply highly evolved apes; we were specially created in the image of God.

Linnaeus based his work on natural theology, the idea that God had created order in the universe and man could understand that Divine Order by studying the creation. He wrote in a preface to *Systema Naturae*, "The Earth's creation is the glory of God, as seen from the works of Nature by Man alone." Linnaeus believed in "fixity of species" (the idea that organisms do not change over time) early in his life, but his plant-breeding experiments showed that hybrids were evidence against the idea that species have remained the same since they were created. Linnaeus found that hybridization could happen above the species level and that organisms in nature were in a state of competition. He explained this as the struggle for nature to maintain the balance that God had instilled in it at creation. New organisms

Creationists recognize certain created kinds that have been present since they were created. Creationists and evolutionists agree that all of the varieties of dogs on earth have a common ancestor—when that ancestor existed is different in the two explanations. This mule is produced by breeding a horse with a donkey—evidence that horses and donkeys are of the same created kind.

that arose were all derived from the *primae speciei* (original kinds) and were a part of God's original plan because He placed the potential for variation in the original creation.

Modern biblical creationists still use the concept of the created kind as a basis for classification and the limit of variation. A group of creation scientists called the Biology Study Group is currently attempting to classify animals within created kinds, or baramins (from the Hebrew *bara*—create and *min*—kind), based on several criteria, including genetic information and breeding studies. The created kinds roughly correspond to the current classification at the family level. However, some kinds may extend up to the order or down to the genus level, since the current system of classification does not take the idea of special creation into account. Any organisms that can interbreed are considered part of the same kind, but those that can't may or may not be. Further research is needed to understand which organisms, both living and extinct, belong to each created kind.

Created Kind (Baramin): the original organisms (and their descendants) created supernaturally by God as described in Genesis 1; these organisms reproduce only their own kind within the limits of preprogrammed information, but with great variation.

> **Note:** Since the original creation, organisms of one kind presumably cannot interbreed with a different kind, but individuals within a kind may have lost the ability (information) to interbreed due to the effects of the Curse.

Classification systems today are still based on physical characteristics, but the natural order is no longer accepted as coming from God. Evidence of design in the natural world is ignored. Secular scientists repeat the mantra that the apparent design is just an accident and that matter and energy are all that can be used to describe how the universe works. Evolutionary relationships are used to reorganize moden classification systems based on the belief that all organisms have a common ancestor.

Phylogeny is the study of the evolutionary relationships between all living organisms. Taxonomists, scientists who classify living things, use different types of diagrams to display the supposed relationships. These diagrams show how organisms are supposed to have descended from a single ancestor. The diagrams come in several forms. The fan diagrams show the organisms with respect to their common ancestors and the relative size of the groups. Phylogenetic trees and cladograms are very similar in that they show evolutionary relationships based on various characteristics. There is much debate in taxonomy about what traits to include when doing the analysis. Different relationships come to light depending on which characteristics are given the most weight in the system of classification. Evolutionists assume that they can construct the complete "tree of life" by including as many traits as possible. Evidence from DNA, anatomy, development, and fossils are commonly used in the construction of these systems.

A major problem with phylogenetic trees and other related models is the lack of evidence that supports the links between known organisms and their supposed fossil relatives. The lines that connect an ancestor to the living organism are mostly imaginary. Very little fossil evidence supports the lines on the diagrams that connect the different kinds of organisms over millions of years, but the lines are often presented as fact. Darwin expected the fossils to show a progression of form, from fish to amphibian, for example, but that progression is missing. The term "missing link" is often used to refer to these gaps and the missing fossils that supposedly fill them. Whenever you see one of these trees, ask, "What direct evidence supports the lines on the tree?" In some cases there are examples of fossils that fit in the sequence, but the vast majority are missing the evidence. The reliability of such a model is called into question when it is based on so many assumptions. The fossil record is discussed in more detail in Chapter 4.

Creationists disagree with the idea of a "tree of life" as evolutionists see it—all life originating from a single, unknown, common ancestor. If we consider the created kinds from Genesis, the picture of life would look more like an orchard—distinct groups of animals showing variety within a kind. The trees in this orchard do not overlap one another or cross one another, representing the limits of variety within the DNA of the created kinds. This view (developed by Dr. Kurt Wise) is confirmed by the evidence from operational science.

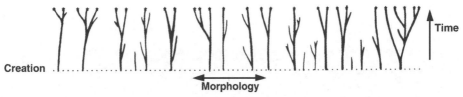

Illustration used with permission from Dr. Kurt Wise and Creation Science Fellowship of Pittsburgh from the 1990 ICC Proceedings, Bob Walsh editor, vol. 2, p. 358.

While new species have been observed to arise, it is always within the limits of the created kinds. The study of this variability and the relationships of animals within the original created kinds is called baraminology. This approach to classifying life is fundamentally opposed to the tree of life. This does not mean that creationists reject the majority of classifications by evolutionary biologists but that the evolutionary history associated with the classifications is rejected. More research is needed in the field of baraminology to understand the relationships within the created kinds. This field of research can make specific predictions about the relationships of organisms based on breeding experiments and improve the current understanding of God's divine order.

Evolutionists use the idea of "molecular clocks" to determine the amount of time that has elapsed since an alleged ancestor split into two groups. This evidence is used to suggest that humans and chimpanzees came from a common ancestor that lived sometime between 4 and 8 million years ago. The operational science behind molecular clocks is based on differences in the DNA sequence or the sequence of amino acids in proteins. The tricky part is interpreting the time involved in these supposed changes. The model of molecular clocks assumes that evolution has happened. Yet, the idea of a Designer

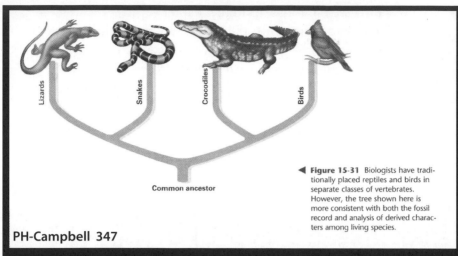

PH-Campbell 347

◀ **Figure 15-31** Biologists have traditionally placed reptiles and birds in separate classes of vertebrates. However, the tree shown here is more consistent with both the fossil record and analysis of derived characters among living species.

Common ancestor

The belief that all of these animals share a common ancestor is based on the assumption that evolution can create new information. The use of DNA and fossils to construct classification schemes has misled people to accept the idea that birds are actually closely related to crocodiles. The Bible describes these two as being created on separate days—not close relatives.

who used similar plans to create similar organisms and molecules is just as reasonable an explanation from a scientific perspective.

Another popular belief is that birds are actually living dinosaurs. Some prominent scientists refuse to accept the idea, but many still find the mystique of watching a dinosaur eating from a feeder in the backyard intriguing. This idea is prominent in the textbooks and media, even though no theory seems to fit the scenario accurately. Whether or not a mechanism for evolving birds from some small theropod dinosaur can be devised, many scientists are sure that it must have happened. It seems that almost all of the new dinosaur fossils are shown by artists to have feathers. Even though there was no clear evidence to support the feathered interpretation, the feathers are added to convince the public that science has found these things to be true. The next time you hear of one of these feathered fossils, ask to see the feather imprints—like the ones preserved so well in the fossilized bird *Archaeopteryx*.

Ultimately, all classification schemes and theoretical relationships are based on man's interpretation of the evidence. Starting with the truth found in God's Word will lead us closer to the true interpretation of the evidence than starting with the fallible ideas of men.

Rather than a tree of life that began with a single common ancestor, creationists believe life started with a certain number of created kinds. All life on earth is a result of the genetic variety in the originally created kinds. As a result, the creationist picture of life would look more like an orchard with many trees, each representing a created kind.

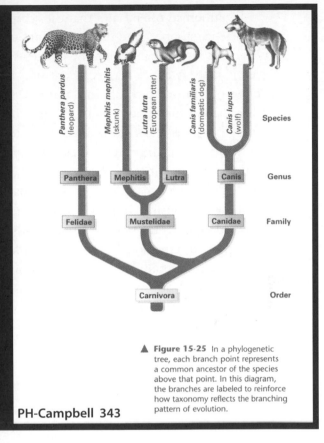

PH-Campbell 343

▲ **Figure 15-25** In a phylogenetic tree, each branch point represents a common ancestor of the species above that point. In this diagram, the branches are labeled to reinforce how taxonomy reflects the branching pattern of evolution.

Reference Articles

2:1 Carolus Linnaeus, Morris, *Men of Science, Men of God*

The modern system of classification is known as the Linnaean system and is based on the work of the creation scientist Carolus Linnaeus. Linnaeus was actually trying to identify the original kinds from Genesis in his research. Linnaeus related the Genesis kind to his category of species and therefore believed in the "fixity of species." Linnaeus recognized that variation happens within the created kinds, not between kinds. Evolutionists often make the false claim that creationists believed, and still believe, that species don't change.

2:2 Arthur Jones on biology, Ashton, www.answersingenesis.org/home/Area/isd/jones.asp

Evolutionists often claim that the acceptance of creation is a "science stopper" and that the actions of God cut off the possibility for studying scientific concepts. This idea, however, is false. A belief in special creation only removes the option of continuous evolution, not the study of the many other relationships among living things. The study of cichlid fish by Dr. Jones showed the amazing variety of characteristics within the cichlid species, including coloration and ability to survive in saltwater. What was also apparent was that the cichlids were a distinct kind of fish that showed no evolutionary relationships in the breeding experiments. The fossil record supports the notion of fixed kinds of fish, with very few supposed transitional forms between kinds of fish. Creationists are not bound to any classification system that rises above the level of kind. Parts of the classification schemes may be correct as they appear today, but more research needs to be done to clarify the relationships.

2:3 How to read an evolutionary family tree, Weston, www.answersingenesis.org/creation/v18/i3/familytree.asp

Charts and diagrams can be wonderful aids in giving clarity and visual reinforcement to a point or lesson one is trying to make. However, these explanatory tools can also be confusing, and in some cases misleading, when the illustrations and their implications are not fully explained. Such is the case with charts that supposedly show the evolutionary relationship of creatures. A typical illustration, such as the one showing insect ancestry, will try to convince you of how a certain group of creatures has evolved from a common ancestor in the past. However, these charts almost always use dotted lines when the supposed evolutionary path is unknown. In these instances, you should simply ignore the dotted lines. By doing so, you will usually be left with a diagram showing that the different types of species depicted have remained basically the same throughout history. Without the dotted lines, these charts simply show the diversity within a kind, revealing that today's creatures haven't really changed from so-called "ancient" ancestors. The dotted lines reinforce the fact that there is no evidence

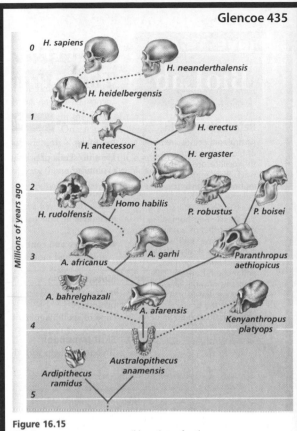

Glencoe 435

When constructing the evolutionary history of life, scientists must make many assumptions. This diagram points out some of those assumptions. The lines represent inferences that many scientists disagree with. The dashed lines represent the "best guess" at the relationships or places where the evidence is contradictory. There are no clear links between the fossils shown when the dashed lines are removed.

Figure 16.15
This diagram represents one possible pathway for the evolution of *Homo sapiens*. Not all scientists agree on the evolutionary pathway.

to prove the existence of a common ancestor. Go to your local library and check all the evolutionary trees you can find. You'll find this a revealing and worthwhile exercise.

2:4 Dinosaurs: phylogenetic chart, www.answersingenesis.org/go/phylogenetic-chart

The next time you see a phylogenetic tree ("tree of life") in a textbook or magazine article, take a look at the fine print. Honest diagrams will make a distinction between the actual evidence and the interpreted information by using shading or dashed and solid lines. In the picture shown on the next page, the lighter lines indicate solid fossil evidence and the darker lines and branching points represent interpretations. So, the real evidence shows stasis, not change.

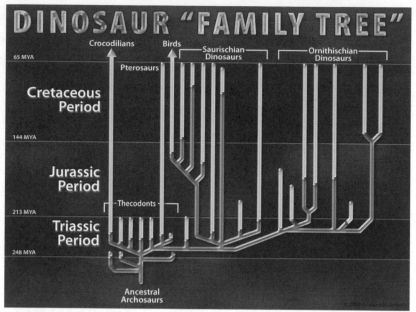

The lighter lines represent actual fossil evidence. The darker lines represent assumptions about relationships. When the assumptions are removed, the evidence fits the creationist orchard model much better.

Dinosaurs were dinosaurs and did not change into something else or from something else. The links between kinds are simply stories about the evidence. The evidence does not prove evolution, as is often suggested.

2:5 Archaeoraptor: featured dinosaur from *National Geographic* doesn't fly, Austin, www.icr.org/article/464

A fossil discovered in 1999 was one of many claimed by a number of scientists and promoted by the media, especially *National Geographic,* to be a feathered dinosaur. The fossil was from a region in China that has been producing many new fossil forms and changing many ideas surrounding the evolutionary history of secular scientists. The fossil was named *Archaeoraptor* and included a bird's upper body structure with fossilized feather imprints but the tail of a theropod dinosaur. The fossil was promoted as proof positive that birds had evolved from dinosaurs. The *National Geographic* article that accompanied the release of the fossil had a model of *T. rex* covered in feathers. This prompted the curator of birds at the Smithsonian Institute to proclaim:

> With the publication of "Feathers for T. rex?" by
> Christopher P. Sloan in its November issue, *National
> Geographic* has reached an all-time low for engaging in
> sensationalistic, unsubstantiated tabloid journalism.

Upon further examination by various experts, it was determined that the fossil was actually a fraud. The apparent difference in the body and tail were actually different— from two different organisms. Despite the fact that this and other "feathered dinosaurs" have been shown to be fakes or misinterpretations, the media and many scientists are still claiming feathers should be shown on fossils that show no evidence of feathers.

2:6 On the alleged dinosaurian ancestry of birds, Camp, www. trueorigin.org/birdevo.asp

The idea of dinosaurs evolving into birds has been around since 1868 when it was first proposed by Thomas Huxley. Since Huxley, the hypothesis has undergone major shifts. Even after 130 years of new evidence, the interpretation is still contested. The presence of two new fossil species, *Protarchaeopteryx* and *Caudipteryx*, has shed little light on the topic. Depending on the bias of the interpreter, these two are either flightless birds or feathered theropod dinosaurs. The presence of short, fibrous structures on a *Sinosauropteryx* fossil is often interpreted as "protofeathers" despite the fact that the existence and structure of these ancestral feathers are completely hypothetical.

In another problematic find, the fossil *Protoavis* is considered to be more similar to modern birds than *Archaeopteryx* but is 75 million years older. This causes significant problems for the theropod theory because the common ancestor would need to be much older than the earliest known dinosaur *Eoraptor*. The plastic nature of the evolutionary theory makes it certain that something else will be put in the role of bird ancestor if the dinosaurs don't fit.

The development of the bird lung is another major issue because no suitable ancestor exists from which the lungs could have developed. Another major question is whether birds evolved from the ground up (cursorial) or down from the trees (arboreal). Many hypotheses have been suggested, but there seems to be no solid evidence for one side or the other. The evolution of birds is an area where scientists have found little to agree on. The special creation of birds and their subsequent variation explain the evidence much better.

2:7 *Scientific American* **admits creationists hit a sore spot,** Matthews, www.answersingenesis.org/go/sciam-sore

Although no feathered dinosaurs have ever been found, many evolutionists believe that birds are living members of a line that began with a dinosaurian ancestor. *Archaeopteryx* is simply an extinct perching bird, not a missing link in the evolution story. Birds and dinosaurs first appear fully formed in the fossil record with no evidence that one evolved into another.

PH-Campbell 567

▲ **Figure 26-10** The ancestor of the feathered animal *Archaeopteryx* may also have given rise to the lineage that includes modern birds.

The old paradigm of bird evolution is admittedly flawed, according to writers of an article in *Scientific American*. The authors admit that evolution does not provide a valid mechanism for creating the amazingly strong, yet lightweight, structures found in birds but not in their close dinosaur cousins. *Archaeopteryx* is discounted as shedding no light on the subject since its feathers look just like modern feathers. There is no fossil evidence of the transition from simple reptilian scales to complex feathers with their many interlocking parts. Evolution cannot explain why feathers would have developed from scales for flight and then developed a new developmental pathway to form them. To explain this, the authors suggest that feathers evolved

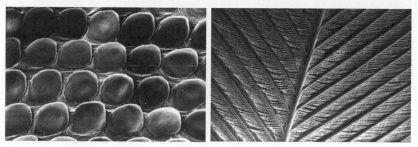

The many differences in the development of feathers and scales makes it clear that scales could not have been remodeled to form a feather. Feathers and hair are much more closely related in development.

before theropod dinosaurs or birds. There is no fossil evidence to support this claim, and the possible reasons for the development of feathers includes camouflage, insulation, protection, and other hypotheses that are not supported by the fossil evidence.

Challenging evolution is not an option, so the evidence just gets reevaluated. The new mode of interpretation is called evolutionary developmental biology, or "evo-devo" for short. According to evo-devo, "the complex mechanisms by which an individual organism grows to its full size and form can provide a window into the evolution of a species' anatomy." In other words, by looking at the stages of feather development in a bird today, we can look for "ancient" dinosaur feathers at the early stages of development. The new concept is based on many assumptions that limit its scientific validity, but it has become popular nonetheless. Challenges to the idea of dino-to-bird evolution continue to plague the proposal, and leading evolutionary biologists cannot even agree on the big picture, let alone the details.

2:8 The demise of mitochondrial Eve, Harrub and Thompson, www.trueorigin.org/mitochondrialeve01.asp

Evolutionary scientists believe that all humans on the earth originated from a small group in Africa over 200,000 years ago. This group included "mitochondrial Eve." Researchers of human origins believe that the ancestry of humans can be traced by analyzing mutations of the DNA contained in the mitochondria of every cell. This mitochondrial DNA (mtDNA) is assumed to be transferred only from mother to offspring in the egg cell. The mitochondria in the sperm do not enter the egg, so they don't become a part of the offspring's cells.

Assuming that the mtDNA sequence of two females should be more similar the farther back in time you go, researchers calculated how long ago the different people groups separated from each other. The African group had more differences from the other groups, so it is assumed that they have had more time to accumulate the mutations. The date was also calibrated by using the assumed divergence of chimps and humans to calculate the rate of mutation.

The mitochondrial Eve idea is only valid if humans receive mtDNA only from the mother and if the rate of mutation is constant and known. Since none of these assumptions are known, the dating method may be invalid. Since recent research indicates that there is mixing of paternal and maternal mtDNA, no conclusion about the rate or origin is reliable—mitochondrial Eve appears to be dead.

The idea that mutation rates are constant and can be used as a "molecular clock" has also been called into question. The dates arrived at by molecular analysis are much older than the dates given when paleontologists interpret the fossil evidence. Many studies have shown that there are different rates of mutation in different populations and in different sections of the mtDNA. This makes the dating very speculative.

Questions to Consider

1. Do the relationships shown in the phylogenetic trees ever change?

2. Since using different characteristics gives different phylogenetic trees, how can you know which tree is right?

2. Can any one classification scheme (phylogenetic tree) be called right or wrong if it is simply an interpretation of the same evidence as other classification schemes?

2. Why do many artists draw feathers on dinosaurs when there is no evidence of actual feathers found with the fossils?

3. Do scientists agree on how dinosaurs turned into birds?

4. Does the fact that a majority of scientists think that dinosaurs evolved into birds make it true? What about those scientists who laugh at this idea?

5. Since different sections of mitochondrial DNA mutate at different rates, how do scientists decide which rate to use when determining evolutionary dates?

Tools for Digging Deeper

(see a complete list in the Introduction)

Bones of Contention by Marvin Lubenow

Buried Alive by Jack Cuozzo

Creation: Facts of Life by Gary Parker

Evolution: The Fossils Still Say No! by Duane Gish

If Animals Could Talk by Werner Gitt

Men of Science, Men of God by Henry Morris

www.answersingenesis.org/go/dinosaurs

NATURAL SELECTION VS. EVOLUTION

We have no acceptable theory of evolution at the present time. There is none; and I cannot accept the theory that I teach to my students each year. Let me explain. I teach the synthetic theory known as the neo-Darwinian one, for one reason only; not because it's good, we know it is bad, but because there isn't any other. Whilst waiting to find something better you are taught something which is known to be inexact, which is a first approximation ...

–Professor Jerome Lejeune, in a lecture given in Paris
on March 17, 1985, translated by Peter Wilders

What You Will Learn

Textbooks present evolution in two different ways—small, observable changes (natural selection, speciation, adaptation) and large, unobservable changes (molecules-to-man evolution). They show evidence for the former and then conclude that this proves that the latter took place as well.

As our understanding of genetics has improved, it has become increasingly clear that mutations + time + chance do not equal evolution. All observed mutations demonstrate a loss of genetic information from the genetic code, or they are neutral. Evolution claims that the process has no direction or goal. If you look at the complexity of the "first" organism, it must be accepted that a massive amount of information has been produced to explain the variety of life we see today. Mutations cannot generate new genetic information; so they cannot be used to explain how evolution has proceeded from a cell with less information than is present in modern cells.

Despite the claims of evolution, the appearance of new species, antibiotic resistance in bacteria, pesticide resistance, and sickle-cell anemia are not evidence in favor of evolution. They do, however, demonstrate the principle of natural selection acting on existing traits—a concept that creationists and evolutionists agree on. The creationist model of how life spread across the globe after the Flood of Genesis uses many of the same principles of natural selection and adaptive radiation that are used in the evolution model. One of the main differences is that the biblical creation model recognizes that one kind cannot change into another and that the changes are a result of variation within the created kinds—not descent from a single common ancestor. As a result of the Curse, genetic mutations, representing a loss of information, have been accumulating, but these do not cause new kinds to emerge. Accepting the idea of a single common ancestor denies the authority of God's Word.

What Your Textbook Says about Natural Selection and Evolution

Evolutionary Concept	Glencoe	PH-Campbell	PH-Miller	Holt	Articles
Evolution is believed by most scientists and is the unifying theory of biology.	9–10, 392–393	T290, T343	T366–367, 367, 369, 386, 410	T6, 9, 276, 283, T410–411	3:1, 3:7
Evolution is not observable on a human timescale.	396–397	—	447	—	3:2, 3:7, 3:11, 3:13, 3:19, 3:24, 3:27, 3:28
Origin of Species provided a unifying explanation for the history of life on earth.	396	39, 297	374–375, T374, 378–379	277–280	3:1, 3:3, 3:4, 3:13, 3:24
Genetic drift in isolated populations	280	327–329	T371, 372, 400, 404–405, T405, 406–409, T407–T409, 439	281, 292, 328	3:5, 3:10, 3:11, 3:12, 3:13, 3:15, 3:22
All life has a single common ancestor.	—	304	369	283	3:6, 3:7, 3:8, 3:13, 3:19
Mutation is the raw material for evolution.	—	310, 314, 243	17, 308, 392, 394–395, T406, 406–409	147, T160, 281, 416	3:1, 3:10, 3:13, 3:15, 3:16, 3:19, 3:21, 3:22, 3:23, 3:28

Evolutionary Concept	Glencoe	PH-Campbell	PH-Miller	Holt	Articles
Mechanisms of evolution	—	—	T262, 376, T376, 393, 401	326, 329, T330	3:10, 3:11, 3:12, 3:13, 3:15, 3:16, 3:19, 3:22, 3:23, 3:27, 3:28, 3:35
Rapid adaptation/ natural selection	—	316	435, 439	290	3:1, 3:5, 3:11, 3:12, 3:13, 3:27
Macroevolution and microevolution	—	311, 324–325	435	—	3:1, 3:12, 3:13, 3:27
Coevolution in symbiotic relationships	—	—	441	362–364, T362, 447	3:7, 3:14
Mendelian genetics	253	206, 310	263–266, 393	162–169	3:10, 3:13, 3:15, 3:21
Polyploidy generally causes death in animals.	273	250	321	—	3:16
Evolution has no purpose or direction.	—	T295	T748	T307	3:4, 3:17, 3:18, 3:19
Evidence is correlated from many areas to support evolution.	403	299–300, 344	386	283, 287	3:7
Natural selection recycles functions of traits.	—	331–333	—	—	3:19

Evolutionary Concept	Glencoe	PH-Campbell	PH-Miller	Holt	Articles
Intelligent design of eyes is not necessary.	—	331–332, 334	—	—	3:2, 3:4, 3:19
Types of mutations	280	—	302, 307–308, T310, T394	124, T123, 180, 219, 327, 216	3:10, 3:13, 3:16
DNA requires proteins to produce proteins.	293	125, 238–241	300–301	208–210	3:20
DNA has evolved to maintain its integrity.	296	—	297	—	3:6, 3:15, 3:21
Beneficial mutations are evidence for evolution.	296–297	314	308	291, 332	3:10, 3:13, 3:15, 3:22, 3:28
Definitions of natural selection, adaptation, and evolution	297	17–18, T16	T2, 16, 381	279, 288–291, 825	1:3, 3:1, 3:13
Definition of evolution	10	298	20, 369	825	1:3, 3:2, 3:4, 3:13, 3:23
Process of evolution	392	290, 305	125, 377, 394, 397, 435, T439, 878–882	—	1:3, 3:13, 3:23, 3:28, 3:35
Natural selection drives evolution.	392	17–18	380, 386, 397–398, T399, 872, 878	—	1:3, 3:1, 3:10, 3:11, 3:12, 3:13, 3:22, 3:23, 3:27

Evolutionary Concept	Glencoe	PH-Campbell	PH-Miller	Holt	Articles
Uniformitarian geology is the basis of the timescale needed for biological evolution.	393, 466–469	295, 356	374–375	277	3:13, 3:25, 3:29
People used to believe the earth was less than 10,000 years old.	367	292	373	277	3:26
Peppered moth and coloration as evolution	397	T296	—	—	3:15, 3:13, 3:27
Pesticide resistance is an example of evolution.	—	307–308	T367, 410	T289, 332, 688	3:13, 3:28
Antibiotic resistance and information in DNA	399, 498	18, 266, 268, 317–319, 364, 370	T367, T386, 403, 410, 487	T279, 289, 449	3:13, 3:22, 3:28
Whales evolved from a wolf-like, hoofed ancestor.	400	300, 344	—	T267, 284–285, T308, 814	3:9, 3:29
Camel and horse evolution series based on fossil record.	400	—	439	—	3:29, 3:30
Homology is evidence of common ancestor.	400, 450	301, 304, 343	384–385	286, 307, 594	3:6, 3:7, 3:33
Vestigial organs demonstrate evolution.	401–402	302	384, T384	T285, 286	3:7, 3:8
Whale pelvis is vestigial.	402	302	—	286	3:8, 3:9
Embryonic recapitulation demonstrates descent from a common ancestor.	402	302–303	384–385, T385	286	3:7, 3:31

Evolutionary Concept	Glencoe	PH-Campbell	PH-Miller	Holt	Articles
Hox genes demonstrate evolutionary relationships.	—	285, 333–334	312, 440, T440	—	3:7, 3:32
Amino acid sequence of proteins determines evolutionary relationships.	403	303–304	865	287, T308	3:6, 3:7
Speciation and adaptive radiation (divergent evolution) demonstrate evolution.	395–397, 404–413	305–306, 568–569	436	—	3:1, 3:5, 3:6, 3:11, 3:12, 3:13, 3:28
Punctuated equilibrium describes gaps in fossil record.	411	329–330	439, T439	282	3:35
Convergent evolution demonstrates evolution of two organisms to look like one another.	413	33, 39, T101, 343, T383, T391, T572	383, T383, 436–437, T436, 828, 832	307	3:6, 3:7, 3:33
Malaria and sickle-cell anemia are evidence of evolution.	508–509	317	347 348, T402	8, T180, 180, 329	3:23, 3:28, 3:34
Diet can be inferred from tooth structure.	843, 844	—	—	—	3:30, 3:36
Genetic engineering shows how humans can interfere with or accelerate evolution.	1076–1079	274–277	322–333, 360	228–243	3:37
Brain complexity is evidence of evolution.	1090–1091	—		—	3:4, 3:6
Viral evolution affects humans.	—	—	T367, 483	934	3:38

Note: Page numbers preceded by "T" indicate items from the teacher notes found in the margins of the Teacher's Edition.

What We Really Know about Natural Selection and Evolution

The ideas of natural selection, speciation, adaptation, and evolution are often used interchangeably by secular scientists. All three of the textbooks reviewed use the terms in this way. When scientists and authors use *evolution* to mean both "change in features over time" and "the history of life on earth," it is difficult to know which definition is being used in each instance. This is often used as a bait-and-switch technique (equivocation). When small changes that arise as a result of the loss of information are used as evidence for molecules-to-man evolution, the switch has occurred. Let's define the terms and see where the switch is happening.

Natural Selection: the process by which individuals possessing a set of traits that confer a survival advantage in a given environment tend to leave more offspring on average that survive to reproduce in the next generation.

Natural selection is an observable process that falls into the category of operational science. We have observed mosquitoes, birds, and many microorganisms undergoing change in relatively short periods of time. New species have been observed to arise. Biblical creationists agree with evolutionists on most of the ideas associated with natural selection, except the idea that natural selection leads to molecules-to-man evolution.

Speciation: the process of change in a population that produces distinct populations which rarely naturally interbreed due to geographic isolation or other factors.

Speciation is observable and fits into the category of operational science. Speciation has never been observed to turn one kind of animal into another. Lions *(Panthera leo)* and tigers *(Panthera tigris)* are both members of the cat kind, but they are considered different species primarily due to their geographic isolation. However, it is possible to mate the two. Ligers (male lion and female tiger) and tigons (male tigers and female lions) are produced (with varying degrees of fertility). These two species came from the original cat kind that would have been present on Noah's Ark.

Adaptation: a physical trait or behavior due to inherited characteristics that gives an organism the ability to survive in a given environment.

Evolutionists often look at a characteristic of an organism and assume that it was produced through a gradual series of changes and call it an adaptation to a given environment. To an evolutionist, legs on tetrapods are an adaptation that arose as a fish's fins became adapted to crawling in a shallow stream, providing some form of advantage. The fins with more bones were better adapted to a life partially lived on the land. Fins that developed bones attached to a pectoral girdle (another set of bones that had to develop) gave

The two tree frogs shown in this figure have been separated by a physical barrier. They certainly had a common ancestor with more genetic variety. As the two populations became separated, certain genes were lost and two new species eventually formed. The text does not explain how they evolved; it just states it as a fact. The formation of new species as a result of loss of information is the opposite type of change required to demonstrate molecules-to-man evolution. This, and other examples found in the textbooks, confirms the biblical creationist model of variation within a kind.

Figure 15.15
When geographic isolation divides a population of tree frogs, the individuals no longer mate across populations. **Explain and Illustrate** *How could geographic isolation result in natural selection and possibly new species?*

A Tree frogs are a single population.

B The formation of a river may divide the frogs into two populations. A new form may appear in one population.

C Over time, the divided populations may become two species that may no longer interbreed, even if reunited.

Glencoe 408

an advantage to those individuals that wandered onto land to find food or avoid predators. The problems with this scenario are in the amount of time such a change would require and the lack of a mechanism to cause the change.

Evolutionary biologists assume, based on geologic interpretations, that there have been billions of years for this process to occur. But if long ages did not exist, the hypothesis cannot be true.

The other requirement, a mechanism for change, is also assumed to exist—even though it has never been observed. We mentioned earlier that natural selection tends to delete information from the population. If natural selection is the mechanism that explains the successive adaptations in the fish fin example above, it must provide new genetic information. To produce the new bones in the fins requires an elaborate orchestration of biologic processes. The bones don't just have to be present; they must develop at the right time in the embryo, have their shape and size predetermined by the DNA sequence, be attached to the correct tendons, ligaments, and blood vessels, attach to the bones of the pectoral girdle, and so on. The amount of information required for this seemingly simple transformation cannot be provided by a process that generally deletes information from the genome.

Biblical creationists consider major structures to be part of the original design provided by God. Modifications to those structures, adaptations, occur due to genetic recombination, random mutations, and natural selection. These structures do not arise from the modification of similar structures of another kind of animal. The beak of the woodpecker, for example, did not arise from the beak of a theropod dinosaur ancestor; it was an originally designed structure. The difference in beak shapes among woodpeckers fits with the idea of natural selection leading to changes within a population of woodpeckers—within the created kind.

Consider a woodpecker pair getting off the Ark. The pair may contain genes (information) for long and short beaks. As the birds spread out into the lush new world growing in the newly deposited soil, they produce offspring that contain both long-beak and short-beak genes. (Although the actual control of beak growth is complex, we will assume that long is dominant over short for this simplistic example.) Areas populated by trees with thick, soft bark would tend to select for woodpeckers with longer beaks. Areas where the

The variation within the woodpecker population is capable of producing birds with longer beaks, but there is no evidence that new information has been produced. This explains how the different varieties of animals and plants that we see today are a result of diversification after the Flood.

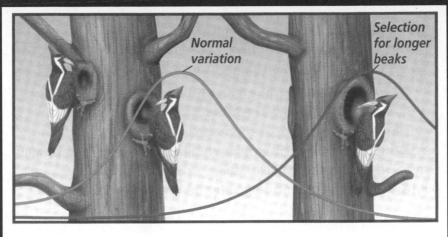

B **Directional selection** favors one of the extreme variations of a trait and can lead to the rapid evolution of a population.

Glencoe 408

bark was thinner and harder would tend to be populated by woodpeckers with shorter beaks. Two new species, with slightly different adaptations, could arise if the two populations were geographically separated. The population of short-beaked woodpeckers would have lost the information for long beaks. No more long-beaked woodpeckers would be produced without a significant addition of genetic information affecting the beak length. The long-beaked woodpeckers would still have the ability to produce short-beaked offspring, but they would be less able to compete, and those genes would tend to decrease in frequency in the population. Due to their isolation, two new species of woodpecker would develop, but within their kind. Observational science supports this type of subtle change within a kind but not molecules-to-man evolution, as we will see in the next section.

Evolution: all life on earth has come about through descent with modification from a single common ancestor (a hypothetical, primitive, single-celled organism).

Evolution is generally assumed to happen as a natural consequence of natural selection. However, no direct observational evidence supports the concept of a fish turning, however gradually, into an amphibian. Evolutionists will argue that there has simply not been enough time to observe such changes. Man has only been recording information that would be useful for a short period of time relative to the immense amounts of time required by evolutionary theory. This raises the question, "Is evolution a valid scientific idea since it cannot be observed in experiments and repeated to show that the conclusions are valid?"

The fact that evolutionary processes, on the scale of millions of years, cannot be observed, tested, repeated, or falsified places them in the category of historical science. In secular science, evaluating historical events is considered just as acceptable as conducting laboratory experiments when it comes to developing scientific theories. Since scientific theories are subject to change, it is acceptable to work within an admittedly deficient framework until a better or more reasonable framework can be found.

A major problem for evolution, as mentioned above, is the huge increase in information content of organisms through time. Evolutionary theory accepts additions and deletions of information as evidence of evolution of a population. The problem is that through the imagined history of life on earth, the information content of the genomes of organisms must have increased dramatically. Beginning with the most primitive form of life, we have a relatively simple genome compared to the genomes that we see today. Mutations are said to provide the fuel for the evolutionary engine. Virtually all observed mutations result in a loss in the information content of a genome. There would need to be some way to consistently add information to the genome to arrive at palm trees and people from a simple single-celled organism—the hypothetical common ancestor of all life on earth. Evolutionists have failed to answer the question, "Where did all the new information come from since mutations are known to reduce information?" You cannot expect evolution, which requires a net gain in information over millions of years, to occur as a result of mutation and natural selection. Natural selection, evolution's supposed mechanism, causes a loss of information and can only act on traits that are already present! (The origin of the information is discussed in chapter 5.)

We have observed the change in dogs over time, but that doesn't mean that evolution has occurred. You can breed wolves to get to chihuahuas, but you can't breed chihuahuas to get wolves—variation in the genetic information has been lost. Darwin used this type of change as evidence without an understanding of the limits of genetic change that are known today.

Creationists agree with the idea of "descent with modification" but not with the notion of a single common ancestor. To accept a common ancestor for all life on earth requires a rejection of the biblical account of creation recorded in Genesis and corroborated by many other Scriptures. The order of events of evolutionary history cannot be reconciled with the account recorded in Genesis 1, without compromising one or the other. The philosophies of evolution and biblical Christianity are not compatible. The examples from the texts below and the articles and books will demonstrate this from a biblical creationist perspective.

Reference Articles

3:1 Is natural selection the same thing as evolution? Purdom, www.answersingenesis.org/articles/nab/is-natural-selection-evolution

Natural selection is generally described as the mechanism that is responsible for molecules-to-man evolution. From a creationist perspective, natural selection is a process whereby organisms possessing specific characteristics survive better than others in a given environment. There is no doubt that natural selection can change the genetic make-up of populations, but is that change able to turn one kind of organism into another? Natural selection involves a loss of genetic information and, therefore, cannot be used to explain how all of the life-forms on earth came to be.

The idea of natural selection was first published by Edward Blyth—a creationist. He suggested that God had created the original kinds, and natural selection acted to conserve, rather than originate, new kinds. Darwin popularized the idea of natural selection acting to create new forms of life over time in the absence of God.

Natural selection can be seen as a mechanism that God used to allow organisms to adapt to changing environments in a sin-cursed world. After death entered the world as the penalty for Adam's sin, animals with detrimental genetic changes would be removed from the population and preserve the original kinds. Evolutionists view the history of life as a single branching tree where all life has come from a common ancestor. Creationists view the history of life as an orchard of trees, each representing one created kind. Natural selection allows organisms to adapt to their environment, but within the bounds of the kind.

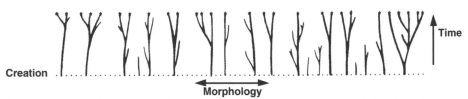

Illustration used with permission from Dr. Kurt Wise and Creation Science Fellowship of Pittsburgh from the 1990 ICC Proceedings, Bob Walsh editor, vol. 2, p. 358.

Using dogs as a simplified example, we could start with two dogs that had medium-length fur. Let L represent the long-fur gene and S represent the short-fur gene. By breeding two dogs with genes for medium fur (LS x LS) we could produce dogs with a variety of fur length

(SS=short, LS=medium, LL=long). If we placed all of these dogs in a cold environment, the long fur would provide an advantage. If all of the short-fur genes (S) were eliminated from the population by natural selection, this would be an advantage to the population. However, if the climate became warmer then there would be no way (other than a mutation of the L gene) to produce short fur—that information was lost from the population. Natural selection can select for a trait and decrease information, but it cannot provide new traits or information.

A similar example occurs with bacteria and antibiotic resistance. Bacteria can become resistant to antibiotics by losing genetic information or swapping genetic information with other bacteria that have the resistance. Antibiotics generally bind to a protein in the bacterium to block its function, eventually causing the bacterium to die. If there is a mutation in the DNA which causes the protein to have a different shape, the antibiotic cannot bind to it and the bacterium lives. To become resistant, the bacterium has lost the information to make the correctly shaped protein. When it is required to compete with other bacteria in the absence of the antibiotic it is less fit and is eliminated from the population.

Back to the dogs, there was likely one pair of the dog kind aboard the Ark. As they stepped out into the environment, the process of speciation began. In the last 4,300 years natural selection has acted on the genetic variation produced by breeding to produce the different varieties of dogs we see around the world today. However, that variation has only led to different types of dogs, never animals of a different kind. The speciation we observe involves a loss of characteristics and information, not the increase in information required to explain molecules-to-man evolution. Natural selection cannot be the driving force of evolution because it results in a decrease of information.

3:2 Is evolution a "fact" of science? Thompson, www.apologetic-spress.org/articles/1985

In the media, textbooks, and scientific literature the occurrence of evolution has become a "fact." The definition of the word *evolution* has also taken on two different meanings that are not equal. Evolution can be used in the sense of change in a species by natural selection. This is often referred to as microevolution and is accepted by evolutionists and creationists alike as good observational science. This type of evolution allows change within groups but not between groups. The other meaning of evolution involves the idea that all organisms on earth share a common ancestor by descent with modification. This idea is commonly referred to as macroevolution. (AiG does not endorse using the terms "microevolution" and "macroevolution." It is not the amount of change that is different, but the type and direction of change that is different. These terms do not clarify that difference.) The two definitions are often used interchangeably. Typically, textbooks show that new species can form—evolution has occurred—so they argue that it is obvious that evolution, in the molecules-to-man sense, must have occurred. The problem is that just because natural selection and speciation have occurred (and there is strong evidence to support such claims) the claim that all life has evolved from a common ancestor is based on many assumptions that cannot be ultimately proven.

People believe the ideas of the evolutionary development of life on earth for many reasons: it is all that they have been taught and exposed to, they believe the evidence supports evolution, they do not want to be lumped with people who do not believe in evolution and are often considered to be less intelligent or "backward," evolution has the stamp of approval from real scientists, and evolutionary history allows people to reject the idea of God and legitimize their own immorality. Evaluating the presuppositions behind belief in evolution makes for a much more productive discussion. Two intelligent people can arrive at different conclusions using the same evidence; so their starting assumptions is the most important issue in discussing historical science.

When we deal with the issue of origins, we must realize that no people were there to observe and record the events.

When scientists discuss the origins of the universe, the earth, or life on earth, we must realize that the discussion is based on assumptions. These fallible assumptions make the conclusions of the discussion less valid than if the discussion were based on actual observation. Almost all biology books and textbooks written in the last two generations have been written as if these presuppositions were true.

Proponents of the evolutionary worldview expect everyone to accept evolution as fact. This is a difficult case to make when the how, why, when, and where of evolutionary history are sharply contested or unknown by the scientists who insist evolution is a fact.

Evolutionists often claim that creation is not scientific because of the unprovable assumptions that it is based on. The fact that evolution is based on its own set of unprovable, untestable, and unfalsifiable assumptions is recognized by many in the scientific community.

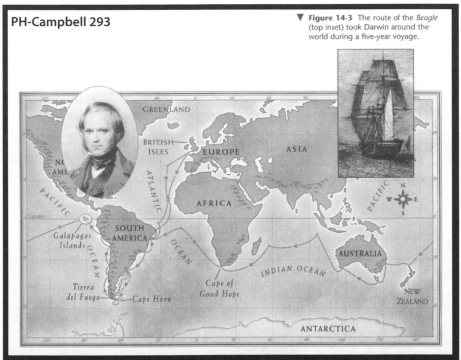

PH-Campbell 293

▼ **Figure 14-3** The route of the *Beagle* (top inset) took Darwin around the world during a five-year voyage.

Darwin developed his ideas over many years after his journey aboard the *Beagle*. The idea of natural selection was recognized by creationists before Darwin used it to remove the glory from God.

Within the scientific literature, the mathematical and chemical impossibilities of the origin of the universe and life on earth are recognized. Many notable scientists, including Sir Fred Hoyle and Sir Francis Crick, have gone so far as to suggest that life originated on other planets or was brought to earth by an intelligent being. These ideas are no less testable than special creation but avoid invoking God as our Creator.

3:3 Why would an evolutionist become a doctor? Mitchell, www.answersingenesis.org/articles/2008/07/21/why-would-evolutionist-become-doctor

It has been claimed by Theodosius Dobzhansky that "nothing in biology makes sense except in the light of evolution." Others have made similar claims, but are these claims justifiable? Many advances in medical science have come from scientists who rejected evolution including vaccinations, antiseptic surgery, and MRI scans. Accepting evolution does not make one a better physician or anatomist. On the contrary, acceptance of evolution raises a very basic question: "Why would an evolutionist become a doctor in the first place?"

The key to evolutionary success is the death of inferior organisms. So, a physician who is an evolutionist interferes with the process when he helps those who are "less fit" survive and reproduce. Darwin himself acknowledged that this situation allows the weakest members of humanity to survive and "propagate their kind." A biblical worldview explains the origin of disease and death and why a physician would want to work against the effects of a sin-cursed world to relieve much suffering through medical science.

3:4 Design without a designer, Parker, www.answersingenesis. org/cec/docs/cfl-pdfs.asp

Darwin grew up in an England that acknowledged a biblical worldview. When he wrote *On the Origin of Species by Means of Natural Selection, or The Preservation of Favoured Races in the Struggle for Life*, he had witnessed a world full of death and disease. How could this be the world created by the God of the Bible? Evolutionary ideas offered people an alternative to a supernatural Creator. Life may appear to be designed, but it is just a product of random changes over millions of years of earth history. This offered people a "scientific" means to reject God and believe in a naturalistic view of the universe. Michael Denton suggests that the chief impact of Darwin's ideas was to make atheism possible and respectable in light of the evidence for a Designer. Darwin's ideas fostered an environment where God was no longer needed—nature was all that was necessary. Darwin's ideas ushered in a pagan era that is now reaching a critical point. The idea that the appearance of design suggests a designer became an invalid argument in the eyes of evolutionists.

3:5 Did God create poodles? Ham, www.answersingenesis.org/go/poodles

Poodles and all other current breeds of dogs are descended from a dog kind that was created on Day 6 and was present on the Ark. The varieties of dogs that we see today, from wolves to coyotes to poodles, are all descendants of the dog kind that came off Noah's Ark. As populations of wild dogs were spreading across the globe, the environment shaped their characteristics through natural selection. As humans began to domesticate dogs, they artificially selected the traits that they desired in populations. The breeds of modern domestic dogs are a result of the diversity that was programmed into the DNA of the original dog kind. All domestic dogs belong to the same species *Canis familiaris* and can interbreed.

Purebred dogs have many genetic problems that result from close breeding of individuals over time to concentrate desirable traits. Many breeds have hip dysplaysia, vision problems, and blood disorders. We know that these dogs could not have been in the Garden of Eden because God called His creation "very good" and He would not have included these genetic mutations in that description. We do know that all of the breeds did come from a very narrow gene pool, and this is confirmed by secular scientists. In the journal *Science*, November 22, 2002, researchers reported, "The origin of the domestic dog from wolves has been established... . We examined the mitochondrial DNA (mtDNA) sequence variation among 654 domestic dogs representing all major dog populations worldwide, ... suggesting a common origin from a single gene pool for all dog populations." It is still important to remember that no new information exists in these mutant forms, only a loss of information from the population, resulting in distinct traits.

3:6 Comparative similarities: homology, Parker, www.answersin-genesis.org/cec/docs/cfl-pdfs.asp

Evolutionists use the idea of "descent from a common ancestor" to explain why the forearm bones of a penguin, bat, and human are so similar. This explanation works for traits in your family, but can it be applied to the history of life on earth? The fact that we use such characteristics to classify organisms into groups does not mean that they are related to a common ancestor. The equally valid alternative is that all of these organisms were created by a common Designer who used the same design principles to accomplish similar functions. Although either explanation may appear equally valid, some instances make the case for a Creator clear.

When structures that appear to be similar to one another develop under the control of genes that are not related, the common ancestor idea fails. Evolution would predict that the structures would be formed from a derived gene that has undergone modification through mutation and natural selection. Frogs and humans supposedly share a common ancestor that would account for the similarity of the limb structures. The problem is that when a frog's digits develop, they grow out from buds in the embryonic hand. In humans, the digits begin as a solid plate and then tissue is removed to form the digits. These entirely different mechanisms produce the same result, but they are not the result of the same genes.

Another challenge to evolutionary explanations is when two structures appear to be homologous but evolutionists know they don't share a common ancestor. Such cases are called "convergent evolution." The eyes of squids and vertebrates are an example where the eyes would be called homologous, but there is no common ancestor to account for the similarities. The common designer argument can once again be used to more easily explain the similarities.

The opposite occurs in "divergent" structures where organisms that appear to be evolutionary cousins have drastically different mechanisms that cannot be explained by a common ancestor. Different light-focusing methods in shrimp provide an example. These systems accomplish the same goal with different and intricate design features—more evidence of their Creator.

Abandoning proof of evolution based on the similarities in large structures, many now look to the similarity in molecular and genetic structure to support evolution. The sporadic presence of hemoglobin in the evolutionary branches of invertebrates is one example. If evolution had occurred, we would expect a predictable pattern—that pattern does not exist. The hemoglobin must have evolved, despite its intricacies, in each of these groups independently. The facts confirm the creationist model of created kinds with great genetic variety and deny evolution from a common ancestor.

The alleged 98% similarity of human and chimp DNA, for example, is often touted as proof of the evolutionary closeness of the two. The 2% difference actually translates into about 60 million base pair differences. The small differences in the genes are actually turned into a large difference in the proteins produced.

The evidence supports the idea of a matrix of specially created organisms with traits occurring where and when they are needed. Discovering the details of this predictive pattern may someday strengthen the validity of the creationist perspective in the minds of skeptics.

3:7 Does homology provide evidence of evolutionary naturalism? Bergman, www.answersingenesis.org/tj/v15/i1/homology.asp

Evolutionists commonly point to the amazing similarity of muscle, bone, and cell structure and function among

The presence of homologous structures can actually be interpreted as evidence for a common designer. Contrary to the oversimplified claim in this figure, the forelimbs of vertebrates do not form in the same way. Specifically, in frogs the phalanges form as buds that grow outward and in humans they form from a ridge that develops furrows inward. The fact that the bones can be correlated does not mean that they are evidence of a single common ancestor.[2]

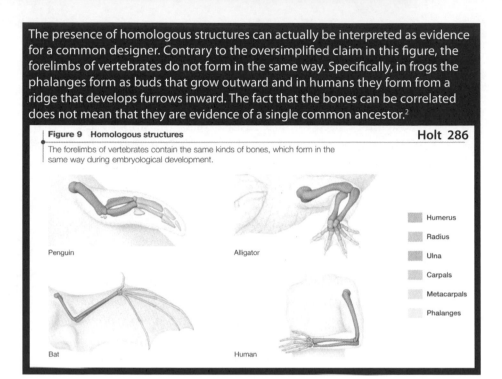

Figure 9 Homologous structures   **Holt 286**

The forelimbs of vertebrates contain the same kinds of bones, which form in the same way during embryological development.

Penguin

Alligator

Bat

Human

- Humerus
- Radius
- Ulna
- Carpals
- Metacarpals
- Phalanges

living things as evidence that all life on earth evolved from a common protocell ancestor some 3.5 billion years ago. Connecting existing animals to the fossil record extends the comparison back to the alleged beginning of time. The idea of homology as proof for evolution is present in almost every high-school or college text on the subject. Evolutionists argue that the only naturalistic explanation for homology is that all of the organisms evolved from a common ancestor. Design arguments are dismissed in naturalistic/materialistic scientific explanations—even though a common designer can explain the similarities as well.

Before Darwin, creationists used the idea of "ideal archetypes" as evidence for a common designer. The features of comparative anatomy were later reinterpreted by evolutionary biologists to argue for descent from a common ancestor. The real question is: "Does the similarity prove that one structure evolved into another?" Since the requirements are similar for living things, homologous structures would be predicted based on a common designer—structures appear similar because they were designed to accomplish the same task. Tires on bicycles look like tires on motorcycles, with design modifications. Kidneys in a skunk look similar to kidneys in a human because they perform the same task and were designed by a common Designer. Evolutionists tend to accept homologies that fit within the evolutionary framework and set aside those that do not support their predictions; supporting structures are called "homologous," while those that don't fit the theory are called "analogous." The existence of similar body plans in organisms that are not considered to be closely related in evolutionary terms is said to demonstrate convergent evolution. The body plan works, so it evolved independently in the two organisms. There are also many exceptions and there is no way to trace many components back to their alleged ancestors due to the incomplete nature of the fossil evidence. Homologous structures cannot exclude the idea of design.

The idea of convergent evolution of analogous structures has trouble explaining exactly how these structures have evolved at different times to be analogous. Wings are supposed to have evolved in at least four different groups as analogous structures. Another example of convergent evolution is the striking similarity between dogs and the Tasmanian tiger (a marsupial). Evolutionists must say that the two evolved independently of one another even though the homology indicates otherwise. Convergent evolution is used as a way to explain away homologies that appear in organisms that aren't supposed to be closely related.

Evolutionists use embryological development, the presence of vestigial organs, and biochemical and genetic homologies to argue for descent from a common ancestor. Yet the patterns expected from the Darwinian model of evolution are not seen in most instances. On the other hand, homologies confirm the creationist model of a common Designer, the Creator God of the Bible.

3:8 Cutting out a useless vestigial argument, Wilkinson, www.answersingenesis.org/creation/v26/i3/vestigial.asp

The idea of vestigial organs has been passed on for over 100 years. Vestigial organs are said to be remnants of

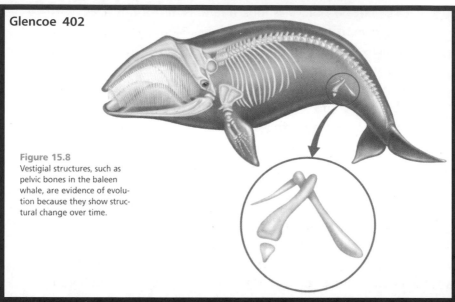

Glencoe 402

Figure 15.8
Vestigial structures, such as pelvic bones in the baleen whale, are evidence of evolution because they show structural change over time.

The pelvic bone in whales serves as an important anchor for muscles of the reproductive organs. Contrary to the claim in this figure, a structure cannot "show structural change over time." The change over time must be inferred from assumptions about the fossil record and evolution. To know if an organ is vestigial, you must know its ancestors and exactly how the organ was used by those ancestors.

organs that were used by an organism's ancestors but are no longer needed, or they function in a reduced capacity in the modern organism. The human appendix is one of the most used, or misused, examples. Just because we do not understand the function of an organ doesn't mean that it serves no function. The appendix was once thought to be an evolutionary leftover, but today we know it serves an important immunological function. Most of the organs that were once thought to be vestigial have been shown to have functions.

3:9 When is a whale a whale? Gish, www.icr.org/article/379

Evolutionists predict the presence of billions of transitional life forms that have existed in earth's history. Despite the presence of 250,000 fossil species, clear transitional forms, which would bolster evolutionary theory, are virtually absent. The situation of transitional forms is glaringly obvious in the case of whales and other marine mammals. The gap in transitional forms was supposedly filled by a partial fossil specimen named *Pakicetus inachus*. Even though the fossil was only a fraction of the skull and a few teeth, the media and scientists portrayed it as a whale-like transitional form. The fact that it was found in a deposit that was likely from a river area puts the interpretation of *Pakicetus* in doubt. (More complete specimens have been found that show *Pakicetus* as a dog-like land animal.)

Fossils of *Ambulocetus natans* were later discovered, and this creature was considered to be a walking whale. Despite the lack of a pelvic girdle (a partial pelvis was found in later specimens), *Ambulocetus* is described as having walked on land much as sea lions do and swimming with a combined motion much as otters and seals do. Why a whale would have hooves on its rear feet and be living near the seashore are questions that are not answered by the fossils.

The deposits containing *Ambulocetus* were found 400 feet higher than where *Pakicetus* was found, but both are supposedly 52 million years old. *Pakicetus* is called the

There is little agreement about the evolutionary ancestor of whales. Some believe it was an ancestor of hippos and pigs, while others believe it was a group known as mesonychids. The contrary nature of the evidence and the lack of transitional forms in the fossil record strengthen the case for distinct groups of created organisms.

▼ **Figure 15-27** When independent types of evidence support the same hypothesis, the hypothesis is strengthened. Fossil evidence and molecular evidence both suggest that whales (left) and the group of mammals that include hippos (middle) are closely related. The painting at right is an artist's depiction of an early ancestor of whales, based on fossils discovered in the early 2000s.

PH-Campbell 344

oldest whale (cetacean), but *Ambulocetus* is supposed to display transitional features as land animals turned into whales. Based on teeth alone, several other wolf-like carnivores (mesonychids) are thought to be ancestors as well. The exact arrangement of these groups is disputed, and some consider the mesonychids to be a branch separate from whales.

This interpretation of scant fossil evidence is very imaginative and totally necessary to support the notion that whales evolved from land animals. Such imaginative claims of evolutionary history have been claimed in the past only to be shown false. Further evidence will certainly change the current thinking in drastic ways.

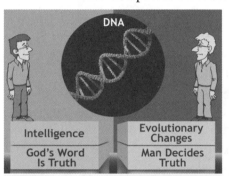

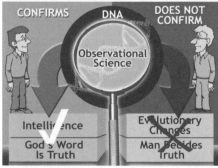

Recent advances in the mechanisms of genetics have made it even clearer that the complex information system found in every living cell must be the result of a Designer. Mutations cannot explain how new information can be formed over time.

3:10 Are mutations part of the "engine" of evolution? Hodge, www.answersingenesis.org/articles/wow/are-mutations-the-engine

This chapter from *The New Answers Book 2* details the common mechanisms of genetic mutation and explains how the mechanisms actually provide examples of a loss of information rather than the creation of new information necessary to explain molecules-to-man evolution. In evolutionary theory, mutations are described as the mechanism that fuels the engine of natural selection, creating new organisms as a result. However, the vast majority of mutations are either neutral or cause a loss of information in the genetic code of an individual.

Evolution teaches that mutations have accumulated over millions of years to increase the complexity of organisms on the earth. The Bible teaches that, as a result of Adam's sin, all of creation is in a downward slide—including the genetic information that is in every living cell. The law against marrying close relations was not given to Israel until Leviticus 18. Up to this point, the accumulation of genetic mistakes was apparently not significant enough to cause genetic disorders in the offspring of close family members. Today, with thousands of years of accumulated genetic mistakes in the human gene pool, intermarriage would be much more likely to produce children with genetic disorders. So it seems that the explanation of a genetic degradation since the Curse of Adam actually fits the evidence better than the evolution model of increasing complexity.

3:11 Does the beak of the finch prove Darwin was right? Morris, www.icr.org/article/1135

While on his journey aboard the *Beagle*, Darwin had an extended stay in the Galapagos Islands. He observed a group of finches that were similar to ones he had seen on the mainland 600 miles away. Darwin concluded that these birds were related to the birds on the mainland but had developed unique traits suited to the islands. The structure of the beaks was one of the key characteristics he studied. This interpretation was contrary to some creationists of his day who believed species could not change.

Darwin's conclusion concerning finches matches that of the modern creationist models and demonstrates the variation within a kind that is observed in nature—the finches are still finches. Studies by Drs. Peter and Rosemary Grant over the past decades have shown that the beak size of the finches changes with the climate of the islands they inhabit. Beaks got larger during droughts and smaller

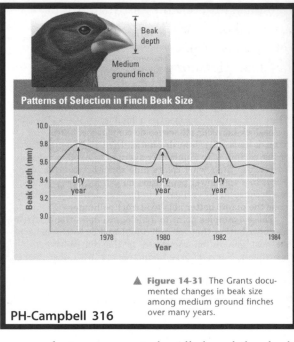

Patterns of Selection in Finch Beak Size

Often cited as evidence for evolution, the finches of the Galapagos actually demonstrate variation within a kind and the limits of change. Note that the graph shows no net change in the beak size of the finch—it leaves off right where it started. This is certainly evidence that populations can change but not that they can change into new kinds.

PH-Campbell 316

▲ **Figure 14-31** The Grants documented changes in beak size among medium ground finches over many years.

during wet periods. All the while, the birds were observed to interbreed. This cannot be considered evidence of evolution in the molecules-to-man sense because there was no net change in the population, even though rapid changes in beak size were observed. The Grants' work is an example of a good study using the principles of operational science arriving at a faulty interpretation based on evolutionary presuppositions.

3:12 Reticulate evolution, Cumming, www.icr.org/article/418

The Grants began studying the finch population of the Galapagos Islands in 1973. They monitored breeding, feeding, and physical data in the birds. The finches' beak shape and size are the main characteristics that are used in classifying them. Even this is difficult with the variability seen in the beaks. One of the biggest problems for the finch studies is the extensive hybridization that occurs between the alleged species. The fact that these hybrids also reproduced should suggest that the three interbreeding species are actually one species. This conclusion was set aside to suggest that hybridization is essential for and accelerates the rate of evolutionary change. The standard species concept was rejected to promote evolution. The hybridization demonstrates the common gene pool that these finches all share and the high degree of variability that was present in the first birds on the islands. The branches and stems in the finch tree of life seem to be more like a thicket with interconnecting lines (termed reticulate evolution). The range of explanations for the process of evolution—it is a "fact" that it has occurred—now includes rapid or gradual, directed or undirected, tree or thicket. The creationist model can still be said to accommodate the data in a much more complete way. Variation within the created kind is confirmed in Darwin's finches.

3:13 Change, yes; evolution, no, Parker, www.answersingenesis. org/cec/docs/cfl-pdfs.asp

The most persuasive—and dangerous—definition for evolution is "change through time." Just because organisms can be observed to change over a period of time does not mean that all life has a common ancestor. If we think of the classic peppered moth example, we started with light and dark moths (*Biston betularia*) and ended up with light—and dark—colored moths of the same species in different proportions. This exemplifies the creationist idea of variation within a kind.

The natural selection that produces the variety of living things we see today began after Adam rebelled against God. The concept of natural selection was published in a biblical context by Edward Blyth 24 years before Darwin published *Origin of Species*. Blyth is forgotten and Darwin is remembered because of the philosophic and religious implications of his idea, not the scientific applications.

Natural selection has been shown to change organisms but always within the boundaries of the created kinds. This type of change is often termed "microevolution," and the hypothetical type of change that turns fish into philosophers is known as "macroevolution." The large-scale changes through time are simply dramatic extrapolations of the observed phenomenon of natural selection. This degree of extrapolation has no basis in operational science. There are limits to the amount and type of genetic change that can occur—no matter what amount of time is allowed. As an illustration: if you can pedal a bicycle at 10 mph, how long would it take to reach the moon? Bicycles have limits that would make this goal impossible regardless of the time you have to accomplish it.

3:14 Henry Zuill on biology, Ashton, www.answersingenesis.org/home/area/isd/zuill.asp

When we look at the world, we see a complex interaction between living things, from bacteria to grizzly bears; all life depends on other life around it. The complexities of relationships in the ecosystems that make up the earth are just as complex as those seen inside each living cell. Biodiversity and the relationships that it incorporates are a hallmark of the design of the Creator. The more diverse and complex an ecosystem is, the more stable it is. Each species in an ecosystem provides a service, but often providers of that service overlap and each species may perform several services. Removal of one of the species has an impact on all other species. This interdependency is supposed to demonstrate how organisms have evolved alongside one another. But how did the first organism survive without the second, and vice versa?

Being created together is a simple explanation, and evolution has great difficulty explaining the many instances of species that absolutely depend on one another for their survival. When cells were described as simple blobs of jelly, it was easy to imagine that they arose spontaneously. Today, the complexity of a single cell defies an origin from simple matter. As we understand more about ecological interactions, it is apparent that the evolutionary relationships that were once assumed to be simplistic are now known to have many layers of complexity. The coevolution of complex symbiotic relationships required the existence of relationships. This provides no answer to the origin of the relationships. If the two organisms were created to coexist, a fine-tuning of the relationship would be expected in the creationist framework. Predators and parasites developed in response to the degraded world after the Flood. The created kinds may have changed, but the general relationships present before the Fall probably remained intact to some degree. The relationships seen are a testament to the Creator who instilled order and flexibility into the system. Evolutionary views cannot adequately explain the symbiotic nature of all living things.

3:15 Genetics: no friend of evolution, Lester, www.answersin-genesis.org/creation/v20/i2/genetics.asp

Mendel and Darwin were contemporaries whose theories were formulated in different ways and clashed with one another. Mendel used careful observations of traits and calculations to develop his theory of inheritance, while Darwin's ideas were based on erroneous ideas about inheritance. Four factors can be considered in genetic variation: environment, recombination, mutation, and creation. It has long been known that environmental effects on individuals cannot be passed on to offspring as the information is not contained in the DNA. Mendel recognized the constancy of traits with variation, while Darwin, to some degree, accepted environmental influence on variation. This is evident from Darwin's discussion of the giraffe's neck becoming longer by "the inherited effects of the increased use of parts."

Mendel showed that traits are reorganized independently when they are passed on to offspring. The variation would not always be evident, but it would only reappear if the trait was present in a previous generation. The amount of variation is limited by the information in the parents. Darwin's finches offer an example of this recombination of traits. Mutations are rare in a given gene, and the cell has elaborate machinery to correct mistakes when they occur. Mutations, when they do occur, tend to be neutral but others are harmful. In the creation model, mistakes in the DNA would be expected to have harmful effects. In evolution, these mistakes are supposed to increase information even though in over 3,000 known fruit fly mutations not one produces a fly that has a survival advantage. Examples of mutations that are beneficial to the individual or population are shown to be a loss of information. Natural selection acts to preserve or eliminate traits that are beneficial or harmful, as the creation model would predict. Creation of organisms by a divine Creator is the only mechanism that is adequate to account for the variation seen in the world today. Each of the created kinds started with considerable genetic variability that has caused the variety of life we see today.

3:16 Copying confusion, Williams, www.answersingenesis.org/creation/v25/i4/DNAduplication.asp

Molecules-to-man evolution requires the production of large amounts of new genetic information. In searching for possible mechanisms, evolutionists have sometimes pointed to the ability of cells to make, and retain, multiple copies of their DNA. If this were the source of evolution, one would expect to find a general increase in the amount of DNA as you move up the evolutionary tree of life. This, however, is not the case. Humans are certainly more complex organisms than bacteria and plants, but they have less DNA in general. The organism with the most DNA is actually a bacterium *(Epulopiscium fishelsoni)* that has at least 25 times as much DNA as a human cell. There are also 85,000 copies of one of its genes per cell. If these extra copies of genes were indeed the raw material for evolutionary mechanisms to act on, this bacterium should be a hallmark of evolutionary adaptation—but it is still a bacterium.

3:17 Man: the image of God, Rendle-Short, www.answersingenesis.org/creation/v4/i1/man.asp

Evolutionists suggest that evolution is a meaningless, undirected process and that humans are a mere accident with no purpose or meaning in the universe. If humans evolved, then there is no eternal life and no God. This obviously flies in the face of Christian beliefs; we were created in the image of God. This view of creation gives our life meaning and purpose. Without God, there is no foundation for morality and each person can do what seems right at the time with no real consequences regarding eternity—eternity does not exist. Man shares characteristics with both animals and God. The Bible equates man and animals on a certain level, but the presence of a spirit and the ability to communicate ideas are attributes man shares with God. We also see God's attributes in human creativity, reasoning, and the ability to express love and pursue the holiness that existed before sin entered the world. The impulse to survive seen in every living thing cannot be described in biological terms; a divine Creator must have instilled this desire in each organism. Evolutionists suggest that the hope of an afterlife is a coping mechanism that has developed as a response to the bleakness of our existence, but God says it is a promise to all. Some will be in the presence of God and others will be cast into Hell.

3:18 Evolution—atheism, Provine, www.answersingenesis.org/home/area/tools/Quotes/provine.asp

"Let me summarize my views on what modern evolutionary biology tells us loud and clear .... There are no gods, no purposes, no goal-directed forces of any kind. There is no life after death. When I die, I am absolutely certain that I am going to be dead. That's the end for me. There is no ultimate foundation for ethics, no ultimate meaning to life, and no free will for humans, either." —Dr. William B. Provine, Professor of Biological Sciences, Cornell University

3:19 Natural selection, yes; evolution, no, Parker, www.answersingenesis.org/cec/docs/cfl-pdfs.asp

The definition of the "fittest" individuals makes the notion of natural selection true based on circular reasoning. The fittest are the ones that survive, and you can tell which are the fittest by seeing which ones survive. (The fact that survival of the fittest is based on circular reasoning does not necessarily mean that the idea is false.) Fitness is controlled by many factors that allow the organism to survive and reproduce. The fastest zebra may be deaf and have a poor sense of smell. This combination would tend to eliminate his genes from a population. The only way to understand fitness is to study the first generation and then track the presence of those traits through time as successive generations are born.

Numerical values can be used to represent the fitness of individuals based on the ratio of individuals with different traits. These numbers can explain fitness, but they have no predictive power—you can only determine the fittest after they survive. Mice that hold still to avoid being seen by a soaring hawk are better able to survive, except when it is safer to run to their burrows to avoid being eaten—each may provide an advantage. If the fact that the survivors survived is used to prove evolution, the circular reasoning becomes a logic problem.

Another misconception is that the fittest variety must be increasing in number. Natural selection can still be acting on a population as its numbers are declining. There is no direction implied in natural selection—you can be the highest scorer (most fit) on the losing team. Competition happens between species (interspecific competition), but natural selection acts within species (intraspecific competition). The struggle for survival is not between lions and zebras, it is within the zebra population. This intraspecific struggle allows for change within kinds, but not from one kind to another.

One shortcoming is that natural selection cannot plan ahead—an advantage one day may

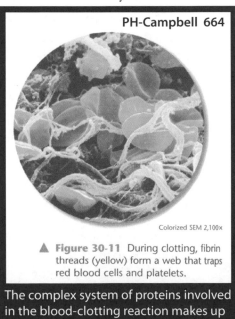

PH-Campbell 664

Colorized SEM 2,100x

▲ **Figure 30-11** During clotting, fibrin threads (yellow) form a web that traps red blood cells and platelets.

The complex system of proteins involved in the blood-clotting reaction makes up an "irreducibly complex" system. If any one of the pieces is missing, the system fails. Evolution cannot adequately explain how such systems could arise.

become a hindrance as the environment changes. This can ultimately lead to the extinction of a population despite its current success in the environment. Natural selection favors specialization into distinct niches; when the environment changes, the specialization becomes a disadvantage. It seems impossible that this process of undirected elimination could lead to an increase in variety and complexity.

Adaptations are usually presented in a way that makes them seem like a natural extension of natural selection. There is limited evidence to suggest that natural selection can lead to new adaptations, but ample evidence shows that adaptations can lead to natural selection. An adaptation must appear before natural selection can act on it. Evolution cannot explain the appearance of these traits, but the Creator provided the variety needed in the original created kinds.

The presence of irreducible complexity in biological systems is another roadblock for naturalistic theories of evolution. It is hard to imagine how you could get to the top of the Empire State Building if you had to jump, but the task becomes easier when you learn that there are stairs. This slow and gradual idea is how evolutionists explain the molecules-to-man idea that once seemed impossible to imagine. This works if all of the steps can be used to build on one another, but what if this were not the case?

Darwin recognized this limit and acknowledged it in *Origin of Species.* In his book *Darwin's Black Box,* Michael Behe describes the biochemical details of several systems that need all of their parts present to function. Since removing one of the proteins involved in blood-clotting causes catastrophic results, the system has irreducible complexity. This irreducible complexity is not only present within living organisms but also between them in ecological interactions. The interaction of fish and shrimp in cleaning symbiosis is one example. A large fish allows a small fish or shrimp to clean parasites from its mouth and then swims off without eating the cleaner. How could this relationship, and other irreducibly complex systems, have evolved one step at a time?

Even if Darwin's ideas can explain the maintenance of

traits and variation within a kind, they do not address the actual origin of the traits in the first place. Darwin used the phrase "from use and disuse, from the direct and indirect actions of the environment" to describe the origin of traits. This is exactly the view held by Lamarck, who is often contrasted with Darwin. Using a trait does not mean it will be passed to the offspring in a different form (stretching giraffe necks is often used as an example). As science has gathered more information about heredity, the idea of use and disuse has been shown to be false.

The origin of this new information is thought by neo-Darwinists to occur by random mutation—random mutations are the raw material for evolution. The cases of fruit fly mutation and flu virus are often used as examples to support evolution. However, these mutations cannot explain the increase or origin of information in living systems. The creationist model—that information was created by the Supreme Designer—fits the observations much better than naturalistic evolution.

3:20 Learning the right tricks about life's origin, www.answersingenesis.org/creation/v13/i4/tricks.asp

A *Scientific American* article admits (way back in 1991) that the "chicken and egg" problem of DNA and proteins has not been solved by the RNA hypothesis. DNA requires proteins to function, and proteins are made from DNA. The actual laboratory observations are highly artificial with a "great deal of help from the scientists." Miller's and Fox's experiments on the origin of proteins and proteinoids, which supposedly produced "protocells," are essentially dead ends. Clever attempts at producing life in the lab only demonstrate that life can be produced by intelligence. The stories of life originating in clay crystals and deep-ocean vents are just stories, with no observational data to confirm them. In all, much more research is needed to even begin to answer the question of the origin of life in a materialistic framework. Creationists need only accept that God has created life and study the changes that have occurred since the creation.

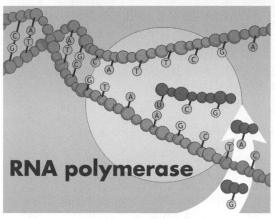

In order for DNA to be transcribed, many proteins must interact with the DNA. The problem is that DNA is needed to make the proteins that are used to transcribe the DNA—a classic example of the "chicken and the egg" dilemma. Evolution cannot explain how such a system could have evolved by random processes acting over time. DNA was created fully functional.

3:21 Startling plant discovery presents problems for evolution, DeWitt, www.answersingenesis.org/docs2005/0406mutation_fixing.asp

An amazing discovery in genetics has shown that a certain plant (*Arabidopsis thaliana*) can actually fix a mutation in a recessive allele even when it doesn't have a copy of the correct sequence in its genome. In a well-designed study, the mutation was shown to be corrected in a "template-directed process," not by random mutations. Organisms that have a better DNA correction system would have a survival advantage, but the irreducible complexity of the system makes it highly improbable that it evolved. This correction mechanism has never been seen before and seems to defy evolution by natural selection. How do you select for the ability to fix a mutation that you don't have? This trait could easily be lost from the population by genetic drift or random mutation in organisms that lack the mutation (assuming it is a DNA-encoded trait). A system that fixes random mutations would stop, or at least slow down, the evolutionary process.

The authors of the study suggest stress induces the repair. Stress has been shown to change mutation rates in certain bacteria, but in the other direction—more mutations are produced to create a variant that can survive the stress. RNA is a candidate for the correction mechanism, but many properties of RNA make it improbable. The

RNA may be acting with other proteins, but more research needs to be done. Evolution is such a plastic theory that a "just so" story will probably come about as a result of this correction mechanism. The problem is that it would be just as likely to fix beneficial mutations as it would harmful ones. A creationist can accept this new mechanism as another way of maintaining the created kinds in light of genetic variability.

3:22 Is bacterial resistance to antibiotics an appropriate example of evolutionary change? Anderson, www.trueorigin.org/bacteria01.asp

[Summary quoted directly from the actual paper] Resistance to antibiotics and other antimicrobials is often claimed to be a clear demonstration of "evolution in a Petri dish." However, analysis of the genetic events causing this resistance reveals that they are not consistent with the genetic events necessary for evolution (defined as common "descent with modification"). Rather, resistance resulting from horizontal gene transfer merely provides a mechanism for transferring pre-existing resistance genes. Horizontal transfer does not provide a mechanism for the origin of those genes. Spontaneous mutation does provide a potential genetic mechanism for the origin of these genes, but such an origin has never been demonstrated. Instead, all known examples of antibiotic resistance via mutation are inconsistent with the genetic requirements of evolution. These mutations result in the loss of pre-existing cellular systems/activities, such as porins and other transport systems, regulatory systems, enzyme activity, and protein binding. Antibiotic resistance may also impart some decrease of "relative fitness" (severe in a few cases), although for many mutants this is compensated by reversion. The real biological cost, though, is loss of pre-existing systems and activities. Such losses are never compensated, unless resistance is lost, and cannot validly be offered as examples of true evolutionary change.

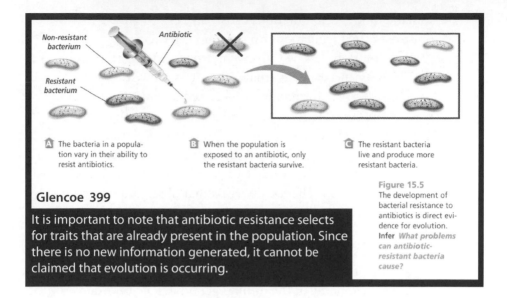

Non-resistant bacterium

Antibiotic

Resistant bacterium

A The bacteria in a population vary in their ability to resist antibiotics.

B When the population is exposed to an antibiotic, only the resistant bacteria survive.

C The resistant bacteria live and produce more resistant bacteria.

Glencoe 399

Figure 15.5
The development of bacterial resistance to antibiotics is direct evidence for evolution.
Infer *What problems can antibiotic-resistant bacteria cause?*

It is important to note that antibiotic resistance selects for traits that are already present in the population. Since there is no new information generated, it cannot be claimed that evolution is occurring.

3:23 Can genetic mutations produce positive changes in living creatures? Demick, www.christiananswers.net/q-eden/genetic-mutations.html

Richard Dawkins used the idea of a "blind watchmaker" to describe how genetics can create new features in organisms through evolutionary processes. Actual observations show that natural selection acts more like a "blind gunman" as mutations occur. Mutations occur when the genetic code of DNA changes and come in many different forms. Only the mutations in the germ cells (eggs and sperm) can be considered in inherited diseases. In a large protein, a mutation at many positions in a gene may cause a defective protein to be formed. In one cholesterol disorder, 350 disease-producing mutations have been documented to cause various problems with cell membrane receptors.

Cystic fibrosis (CF) is caused by a group of mutations in an ion pump in the cell membrane. The protein consists of 1,480 amino acids and the deletion of three bases at codon 508 causes most cases of CF. Nearly 200 other mutations have been shown to cause CF as well. Cancer is another disease that demonstrates the danger that mutations can cause to organisms. Many types of germ-line and somatic (body) cell mutations cause the cells to grow without the normal regulations on size and cell division.

If evolution has led from microbes to man, there should be some evidence that mutations can cause such an increase in information. Sickle-cell anemia is often used as an example to support Darwinian evolution, but the mutation clearly causes a loss of normal function with no new ability or information. Cancer cells are fitter than other cells around them but can hardly be considered as proof of evolution. The fact remains that observational science shows that mutations cause negative effects without a single example of a mutation that improves the function of a protein in support of evolution.

If we start from the Bible, the effects of mutations and the continued decay of the human genome is a clear example of the Curse that resulted from Adam's sin. The human genome will become increasingly corrupted as time passes. Christ's return and the fact that He conquered death offers the world hope for the future.

3:24 What does the fossil record teach us about evolution? Van Bebber and Taylor, www.christiananswers.net/q-eden/edn-c006. html

When deciding if the fossil record actually supports the evolution of life on earth, many factors need to be considered. Animals and plants appear very abruptly in the fossil record. Evolution would predict the fossils we find should show a vast array of transitional forms—few if any are found. Despite the extensive number of fossils found, it is believed that few new fossil types will be discovered. The lack of order in the geologic layers presents another challenge for evolutionists. The fossil record is much more consistent with the occurrence of a global Flood and special creation than with an evolutionary history.

3:25 Evidence for a young world, Humphreys, www.icr.org/article/1842

Many of the dating techniques that can be used to

determine the age of the universe and the earth point to a maximum amount of time less than the billions of years required by naturalistic evolution. Galaxies wind themselves up much too fast to be billions of years old. There are too few visible supernova remnants. Comets disintegrate too rapidly and have no mechanism to reform. There is too little sediment on the sea floor to account for erosion and not enough sodium in the sea to account for billions of years. The earth's magnetic field is decaying too rapidly. Rock layers are bent to extreme degrees, suggesting they folded rapidly while still soft. DNA and other biologic materials should decay and not be found in fossils—bacteria alleged to be 250 million years old should have no intact DNA left, yet they were able to grow.

Radioactive halos present in rocks show a time of rapid radioactive decay in the past. Too much helium resides in minerals that are supposed to be very old. Carbon-14 is found in diamonds and coal that are supposed to be millions or billions of years old. There are too few skeletons of Stone Age humans to support the alleged 200,000-year timespan. Agriculture and historical writings have been around for too short a period. In combination, this short list demonstrates that many dating methods defy the billions of years needed to support evolution's house of cards.

3:26 Gallup poll on creationism, poll.gallup.com/content/default.aspx?ci=18748

A poll conducted by the Gallup Organization in 2005 found that 29% of Americans believe that creationism (including life originating 6,000 years ago) is definitely true with respect to explaining the origin of life on earth. About 20% consider evolution definitely true, and only 8% believe intelligent design is definitely true. The results also indicate that many people still have mixed views on the compatibility of evolution and creation.

By 58% to 26%, a majority of Americans express their belief in creationism; by 55% to 34%, a majority also accept evolution. But 32% of Americans tend to reject intelligent design, while 31% say it is probably true. The statistics make it clear that many Americans are blending ideas of creation and evolution together in an attempt to make sense of the conflicting messages. (Standing on the authority of the Bible will lead to an acceptance of creationism as the only position consistent with Scripture.)

3:27 Natural selection, Parker, www.answersingenesis.org/cec/docs/cfl-pdfs.asp

Darwin based his idea of natural selection on the changes he observed in selective breeding by farmers and animal breeders. It can be observed that artificial selection can lead to the expression of hidden traits. Darwin suggested that if man can produce such changes in a short time, over millions of years natural selection could produce entirely new species. Darwin was right about the ability of natural selection to change populations, but he was wrong about the extent of change that could occur.

A popular example in textbooks is the case of the peppered moth. The proportion of moths of different color was shown to change as pollution changed the environment they lived in. It has also been recently revealed that the photos of moths showed dead or stunned moths glued to trees and that the moths do not land on the trunks.

Problem-Solving Lab 15.1

Interpret Data

How can natural selection be observed? In some organisms that have a short life cycle, biologists have observed the evolution of adaptations to rapid environmental changes. Scientists studied camouflage adaptations in a population of light- and dark-colored peppered moths, *Biston betularia*. The moths sometimes rested on trees that grew in both the country and the city. Moths are usually speckled gray-brown, and dark moths, which occur occasionally, are black. Some birds eat peppered moths. Urban industrial pollution had blackened the bark of city trees with soot. In the photo, you see a city tree with dark bark similar to the color of one of the moths.

Biston betularia

Glencoe 397

The peppered moths used as an example in many textbooks have actually been exposed as a fraud. Dead and sedated moths were placed on tree trunks where the moths were never observed to rest. Despite the fraud, this is a clear example of natural selection, not evolution.

Despite the fraud, the concept still fails to prove evolution in the molecules-to-man sense.

3:28 Mutation, yes; evolution, no, Parker, www.answersingenesis. org/cec/docs/cfl-pdfs.asp

There are three limits to accepting mutations as a mechanism for molecules-to-man evolution. First, there are mathematical limits to the probability of evolution occurring. Mutations occur once in every 10 million duplications of DNA, so it is very likely that every cell in your body contains at least one mutation since you were born. The problem for evolution is that you need multiple, related mutations to cause a change in a structure. If mutations occur at a rate of one in 10^7, the odds of getting two related mutations is 10^{14}. The likelihood of evolution quickly becomes unreasonable. In bacteria that are resistant to four different antibiotics, the probability would be 1 in 10^{28}. It has been shown that the bacteria already had the information for resistance built into them—the trait was selected for, not created by mutations. Those bacteria that do become resistant by mutation are less fit and don't survive outside relatively sterile environments. This is not evidence for evolution.

Second, mutations are moving in the wrong direction to support the advancement of complexity required by evolution. Almost every mutation we know of has been identified based on the disease it causes. Mutations explain the decline seen in genetic systems since the Fall of mankind in Adam. The time, chance, and random mutations simply serve to tear things apart. Shortly after creation, there would have been few genetic mistakes present in the human population, and marrying a close relative would not have been a problem. Today, the likelihood of a shared mutation causing a disease is too great a risk to allow close marriages.

The advantage of avoiding severe malaria symptoms by those with sickle-cell anemia is often given as evidence of beneficial mutations. The overall effect of the mutation is not beneficial to the human race, however, and will not lead to a more fit population.

Third, mutations can only act on genes that already exist. Natural selection cannot explain the origin of genes because there was no information for natural selection to act on. Mutation and natural selection simply produce variation within a kind—just as the biblical creation model suggests. No genetic mechanism can increase the amount of information that is needed to demonstrate evolution from particles to people. Mutations do not add information to an organism's genome. Thousands of mutations would need to add information to change even "simple" cells into more complex cells. Even when genes mutate, they still pair up with similar alleles and are controlled by the same regulators. Mutations may affect the degree of a trait, but they do not cause new traits.

It is not the amount of time or the number of mutations, but the direction of change and the origin of information that are the biggest stumbling blocks for evolution. All of the evidence continues to point to the design and information originally provided by the Creator.

3:29 Scientific roadblocks to whale evolution, Sherwin, www. icr.org/article/433

One of the popular stories of evolution tells of how land animals evolved into whales and their cousins. Darwin suggested that a race of bears became more and more aquatic until they were whales. Other stories are full of details that have no basis in any facts. To produce whales from small land mammals would require countless changes. These gradual changes are not preserved in the fossil record to any degree.

There are many suggested ancestors to the whales, from wolf-like creatures to hippos. All require amazing changes that must have happened at an astonishing rate to fit the evolutionary timescale. Blubber, temperature regulation, special metabolism, countercurrent blood flow, and other functions would have to be present before natural selection could act on these traits. The development of one- or two-holed breathing structures stretches the limits of the evidence in fossils. Whale tails move up and down, while the alleged ancestors did not have this ability. The pelvis would have to be minimized while the flukes were expanded. The fossils to document these changes are absent.

The lack of consistency between molecular data and morphological data is a strike against evolution in general. The inconsistency is evident where certain proteins suggest whales and hippos should be grouped together, while the fossils suggest a carnivorous ancestor for whales. Neither natural selection nor mutations are sufficient to explain the alleged transformation from anything to a whale. The biblical model still provides the best explanation.

3:30 Camels—confirmation of creation, Weston, www.answersingenesis.org/creation/v19/i4/camels.asp

Many features of the camel point to amazing design. The features include the ability to go without food and

The actual fossils evidence is not presented as support for the drawings. When you see a picture like this, ask yourself, "What did the bones look like and where did the details come from?" The striped fur and the hump are drawn to give the impression of progress, but the fossils do not support the drawings. Keep in mind that the artist has an objective when they are drawing the pictures. This series seems to replace the once-popular horse series that was shown to be false.

Table 15.1

Fossils are used by scientists to understand how camels evolved.

Glencoe 400

Table 15.1 Camel Evolution					
Age	Paleocene 65 million years ago	Eocene 54 million years ago	Oligocene 33 million years ago	Miocene 23 million years ago	Present
Organism					
Skull and teeth					
Limb bones					

water for extended periods, to avoid sweating by increasing body temperature, and to consume large amounts of water to rehydrate. The alleged evolutionary series of the camel is only possible because we have living examples today. If assembling fossils in a sequence is like a puzzle, you need to know what the picture looks like before you start, or you are just randomly placing the pieces. The *Camelops* fossils of 3.5 million years ago are described as true camels, but even they haven't changed much in the supposed expanse of time.

3:31 Something fishy about gill slits! Mitchell, www.answersin-genesis.org/articles/2007/03/14/fishy-gill-slits

German scientist Ernst Haeckel popularized the idea that "ontogeny recapitulates phylogeny"—human embryos go through a fish stage, an amphibian stage, a reptile stage, and so on. Haeckel made fraudulent drawings of embryos to provide evidence for his belief. One feature that is often

The presence of similar structures in human and bird embryos are supposed to be evidence for a common ancestor. However, a common designer using certain design features to accomplish different functions is also a legitimate explanation. Many embryologists have abandoned the idea of "embryonic recapitulation," but it still remains in the textbooks as evidence for evolution.

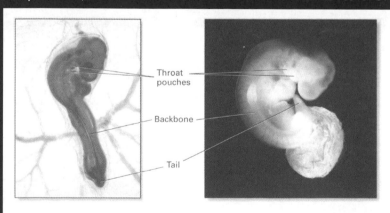

Throat pouches

Backbone

Tail

▲ **Figure 14-15** Even at this early stage of development, the kinship of vertebrates is evident. Notice, for example, the throat pouches and tails of both the bird embryo (left) and the human embryo (right).

PH-Campbell 303

pointed out when comparing embryos is the "gill slits." In human embryos, these structures have nothing to do with the formation of gills. These "slits" are actually folds in the tissues in the neck region. More appropriately called pharyngeal (throat) arches, the clefts and pouches of this region are never related to breathing, but actually become part of the ear and the bones, muscles, nerves, and glands of the neck. Rather than pointing to the evolutionary relationship between humans and worms, this superficial similarity in embryos is just that.

3:32 Hox hype, DeWitt, www.answersingenesis.org/docs2002/0215hox_hype.asp

Homeobox (hox) genes are the switches that control where and when a feature develops. Evolutionists use hox genes to describe how major evolutionary changes could have occurred—six-legged insects could have evolved from shrimp if the genes that control leg development were mutated. A reduction in the number of legs over time fits within the creationist framework of loss of information, but it does not explain the origin of the legs in the first place. Hox gene mutations that cause flies to grow extra wings are not accompanied by the muscular and other changes needed to make those wings functional—the extra wings would actually hinder the fly from flying, and the defect would be eliminated from the population. No matter how dramatic the changes may seem, losing or misplacing parts cannot explain the gain of information needed for molecules-to-man evolution.

3:33 Living light, Sherwin, www.icr.org/article/231

Those who have seen fireflies are familiar with bioluminescence—a phenomenon found throughout the biological world. The chemical reaction that produces this "living light" is found in algae, worms, insects, fungi, and genetically modified organisms. Evolutionists attempt to explain the broad array of living things that have this ability with convergent evolution. This ability, which involves at least two chemical reactions and several compounds, would have had to evolve independently at least 30 different times to explain its existence in living things. The separate lines of descent would have to have undergone the same random changes at hundreds of genetic steps—statistically impossible. The convergence of this and other traits is solid evidence for a Creator who used a common design.

3:34 Sickle-cell anemia does not prove evolution, www.answersingenesis.org/go/sickle-cell

It is commonly believed that the abnormally high presence of sickle-cell anemia (SCA) in African populations is evidence of evolution. It is true that individuals with SCA do not suffer as severely when they contract malaria because the blood cells are not as suitable for the malaria pathogen. This does not mean that there are not other factors (marriage customs, diet, viral infections, and social factors) that influence the occurrence of SCA in these populations. Using natural selection alone ignores the other social implications and leads to a misunderstanding of the true nature of the disease. Natural selection plays a part in the high frequency of those who carry the SCA gene, but it is not the only factor. Even though natural selection is shown to be a

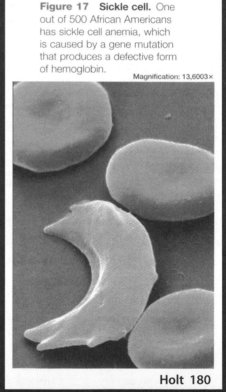

Figure 17 **Sickle cell.** One out of 500 African Americans has sickle cell anemia, which is caused by a gene mutation that produces a defective form of hemoglobin.

Magnification: 13,6003×

Holt 180

The fact that sickle-cell anemia occurs at a higher rate in populations where malaria is common does not provide evidence for the type of changes required for molecules-to-man evolution.

factor, it does not demonstrate the type of uphill evolution required to validate evolutionary theory.

3:35 Vertebrates: animals with backbones, Parker, www.answers-ingenesis.org/cec/docs/cfl-pdfs.asp

If animals have evolved from a common ancestor, there should be a multitude of missing links to demonstrate the gradual changes. One commonly cited example is *Archae-opteryx*. *Archaeopteryx* appears to have a blend of reptilian and bird characteristics—exactly what evolution would predict. The features of *Archaeopteryx* can be found in various birds, and the presence of wings and feathers doesn't tell you how—or if—they evolved from other structures. These complex features appear suddenly and fully formed in the fossil record. *Archaeopteryx* is a true bird with odd features, not a missing link.

The fraudulent "feathered dinosaur" (*Archaeoraptor*) that was published in *National Geographic* is another example of a missing link that has been abandoned. Many of the other Chinese fossils that are supposed to be the ancestors of birds actually occur too high in the rock layers. To be included as a transitional form, fossils must be in the right sequence and have intermediate features. Of the thousands upon thousands of transitional forms that must have existed, only a handful of fossils are possibilities.

Recognizing the failure of the fossil record to display the gradual nature of Darwinian evolution, Stephen J. Gould resurrected the idea of evolution in big jumps known as "punctuated equilibrium." Major remodeling of body plans could occur if regulator genes caused multiple changes at once. This would explain gaps in the fossil record, but it is not supported by observational science. Even if these creatures were born, what would they mate with? The exact mutations would have to occur simultaneously and in close proximity—a highly improbable situation. Those scientists who support this idea at least admit that the links are missing.

Gradualists say that punctuated equilibrium is absurd and evolution cannot happen that fast. Punctuational evolutionists point to genetic limits and fossil gaps and say that evolution didn't happen slowly. The creationist can simply agree that both are correct—life was designed by the Creator. The variation that we see within created kinds supports this notion.

3:36 Unexpectedly vegetarian animals—what does it mean? Hodge, www.answersingenesis.org/articles/2009/06/02/vegetarian-animals

The fruit bat has teeth that are designed for eating fruit, not meat. Evolution would say that the bat evolved from a meat-eating ancestor, but that is based on assumption. Many other animals that are predominantly herbivores have a similar tooth structure.

In today's world of death and suffering, it is easy to forget that there was a time when animals did not eat one another. In the beginning of the creation, animals were created as vegetarians. After the Fall, many animals began eating one another. The preserved stomach contents of animals fossilized in the Flood give us evidence of this. Spiders today primarily eat insects, but there are spiders that eat pollen and sip nectar. A recently discovered spider actually feeds on acacia trees rather than the ants that live alongside of it.

Lions might be the most popular carnivores, but several have been documented to live on vegetarian diets. There is a vulture in Africa that primarily eats palm nuts. The pacu, a cousin of the piranha, feeds with its razor-sharp teeth on seeds and fruits that fall to the water. Just because animals have teeth or other structures that make them appear to be suited for eating other animals does not mean that is the case. These vegetarian "carnivores" could have easily survived without meat in the original creation.

3:37 Virus "evolution" benefits mankind? Purdom, www.answersingenesis.org/docs2006/0222virus.asp

Humans have developed the technology to manipulate the genetic code of many different organisms, but is it evidence for evolution? The ability to change a virus used to deliver gene therapy was recently described as "directed evolution." By selecting for viruses that could evade the immune system and then copying those with intentional mistakes, scientists produced a virus that avoided immune defenses. Since the viruses already had the information to avoid the immune system, this cannot be considered evidence for molecules-to-man evolution—no new information was produced. The advantage provided by genetic mistakes in viruses in nature does not demonstrate that new information is added but that the preexisting information is selected for or against by the environmental conditions. This research did not rely in any way on evolutionary principles but the observed properties of genetic information that fits consistently in the creationist model of life.

3:38 Genetic variance of influenza type A avian virus and its evolutionary implications, Kitner, www.answersingenesis.org/go/bird-flu-evolving

The bird flu, caused by a type A influenza virus, has been in the media, and many are afraid that it will "evolve" into a form that will cause a pandemic in humans. The virus that causes disease is made up of eight RNA segments which code for its protein components. The bird flu spreads so rapidly because it is often present in migrating birds that show no symptoms. These birds pass the virus to domestic birds that do not have a natural immunity, which leads to outbreaks in the domestic populations. The ability of the virus to constantly change its protein coat makes vaccination virtually useless. The genetic variation within the virus is observable, but it does not support evolution in the molecules-to-man sense. The genes are simply slight variations that code for a protein that performs the same function. Viruses can change, but they cannot evolve to become anything other than viruses.

Questions to Consider

1. What mechanisms do scientists use to explain how mutations can produce new information to make organisms more complex, when virtually all mutations cause a loss of information or no change at all?

2. Since information cannot be created from matter by purely natural mechanisms and since it is not a part of the material universe, how did information originate? By what mechanism is new information added to genomes in evolutionary history? Can the information gain be demonstrated experimentally?

3. What direct fossil evidence is there that fish could have evolved into amphibians? Could the alleged transitional fossils be interpreted in multiple ways?

4. When two lines of evidence contradict each other (e.g., if DNA suggests one evolutionary relationship and anatomy suggests a different relationship), how do scientists decide which line of evidence is more compelling?

5. Why is evolution the key to understanding biology? Why is it necessary to know where the eye evolved from to understand how it works and how to treat it when it has a disease?

6. Why do examples of natural selection get equated with evolution when evolution is not observable and natural selection is?

7. Why do biology textbooks include the photo of the peppered moth when scientists have shown it to be a fraud?

8. Should we accept everything that the text tells us about evolution when the textbooks are constantly being changed and updated?

9. If evolution is not directed by a purpose, would it be safe to say that human existence is purposeless? What is the basis for truth and morality if human life is a byproduct of evolutionary processes (random interactions of lifeless chemicals)?

10. Are humans more special or important than any other organism if there is no such thing as higher and lower animals in an evolutionary framework?

11. Is it possible to know the original function of an organ that is called vestigial, like the appendix, when most tissues are not preserved in fossils and the ancestor cannot be examined? It would seem that there are many assumptions involved in making such a claim.

12. Does evolution predict stasis or progress? Why are so many "living fossils" found that have remained the same for hundreds of millions of years while other species have evolved relatively rapidly?

13. There seem to be many different definitions of evolution; do all scientists agree on what evolution is? Which view of evolution is correct (punctuated equilibrium, neo-Darwinism, Darwinism, etc.)?

14. Why do scientists consider homologous structures evidence of a common ancestor when they seem to fit the expected pattern, but scientists call them examples of convergent evolution when they don't fit the pattern?

15. What types of evidence would evolutionists accept as evidence against evolution?

Tools for Digging Deeper

(see a complete list in the Introduction)

The New Answers Book 1 & 2 by Ham et al.

The Biotic Message by Walter ReMine

Creation: Facts of Life by Gary Parker

Darwin on Trial by Phillip Johnson

Darwin's Black Box by Michael Behe

Darwin's Enigma by Luther Sutherland

Evolution: A Theory in Crisis by Michael Denton

Evolution: The Fossils Still Say No! by Duane Gish

If Animals Could Talk by Werner Gitt

In Six Days by John Ashton

In the Beginning Was Information by Werner Gitt

Genetic Entropy and the Mystery of the Genome by John Sanford

The Lie: Evolution by Ken Ham

Not by Chance by Lee Spetner

On the Seventh Day by John Ashton

04

UNLOCKING THE GEOLOGIC RECORD

Everybody knows fossils are fickle; bones will sing any song you want to hear.

—Shreeve, J., Argument over a woman, *Discover* **11** (8):58, 1990

Contrary to what most scientists write, the fossil record does not support the Darwinian theory of evolution because it is this theory (there are several) which we use to interpret the fossil record. By doing so, we are guilty of circular reasoning if we then say the fossil record supports this theory.

—West, R. (Kansas State Univ.),
Paleontology and Uniformitarianism, *Compass* **45**:216, 1968

What You Will Learn

Evolutionists hold up the fossil record as evidence that evolution has taken place over the billions of years of earth history. Evolution is based on the presupposition that those billions of years have occurred. Using radiometric dating and other dating methods, evolutionists claim that life began on earth about 3.5 billion years ago. Creationists, using the Bible as a starting point, claim that the earth is only about 6,000 years old—and there is abundant evidence that is consistent with this claim. The huge difference is because evolutionists accept uniformitarian (slow and steady) assumptions while creationists believe the worldwide presence of rock layers containing fossils can best be explained by catastrophic processes (rapid and abrupt). Observational science has shown that fossils and rocks can form rapidly. The idea of a young earth is not compatible with evolution.

The sequence of fossils and the rock layers are supposed to strengthen the case for evolution. Two problems with this idea are that many of the fossils occur in the wrong layer sequence and that the rock layers are often bent to an amazing degree—both are evidence for a recent catastrophe. The geologic record should also be riddled with thousands of transitional forms that show a slow and gradual progression, as well as the many dead ends in the evolutionary story. The absence of these transitional forms and the abrupt appearance of many complex life forms is evidence that these groups were created by God and then later buried in the global Flood of Noah's day. The recent discoveries of dinosaur bones with "fresh" tissue and fossilized amphibian bones with intact bone marrow clearly point to the fact that dinosaurs lived recently. In fact, they shared the earth with humans beginning on Day 6 of creation, just thousands of years ago. That history is accurately recorded in the Bible. Starting with the wrong presuppositions has led people to believe in the wrong history of the earth. Evolution fails to provide a consistent account of earth history, while the biblical creation model puts the evidence into a consistent framework.

What Your Textbook Says about the Geologic Record

Evolutionary Concept	Glencoe	PH-Campbell	PH-Miller	Holt	Articles
Soil and sedimentary rocks form slowly over millions of years.	153	299, T299, 392	374, 416, 500	—	3:24, 4:1, 4:2, 4:3, 4:6, 4:8
The sequence of fossils in the geologic strata is proof of evolution.	366, 736	335–336, 564	373, 417	283	3:24, 3:35, 4:4, 4:5
Species only occur for a short time in earth's history.	—	329, T337	417, 435	—	4:5
Fossil plants have been found with chlorophyll and dinosaur bones with blood components.	—	335	—	—	4:6
Combining the evidence from rocks, fossils, plate tectonics, and chemistry provides a solid basis for evolutionary theory.	368	335	—	252, T252, 272–273	3:6, 3:24, 3:29
The earth formed about 4.5 billion years ago. Life first appeared 3.9 billion years ago.	369–370, 377	300, 356	410, 423, 447	252	4:7
"Living fossils" show that evolution can happen at different rates.	371	522, T526	416, T416, 567	—	4:9
Fossil teeth can help us understand diet and classification.	371	346	—	709, 802	3:30, 3:36

Evolutionary Concept	Glencoe	PH-Campbell	PH-Miller	Holt	Articles
Grand Canyon formed by slow erosional processes over millions of years.	—	295	T375	—	4:10, 4:11
Rock layers can be given relative dates; older rocks are lower in the strata. But absolute dates can be found by radiometric dating.	372, 736	299, 336–339, 351	20	283	4:12, 4:15
Radiometric dating provides a reliable way to know the age of rocks.	372–375, 387	338, 340	T6, 36, 420	252–253, T253, T284, 285	4:12, 4:15
Fossils form slowly over millions of years.	373	—	418	284–285	4:6
Geologic time relates the 4.5 billion year history of the earth.	374–375, 556–557	T294, 336–337, T356, T514	129, 422–423, 624–625	T250–251, T258, 258–268, T714	4:12, 4:13, 4:14
The geologic column displays the history of life on earth in the sequence of layers.	375–377, 1084–1085	300, 336	382, 419, T772	—	3:24, 3:29, 4:13, 4:14
Fossils show a gradual change as you move up the geologic column.	411	295	383, 410, 421, T920	—	3:24, 3:29, 3:35, 4:13
The Cambrian explosion represents a great diversification in evolutionary history.	377	336, 515, T515	430, 746	262, T262	3:24, 4:16

Evolutionary Concept	Glencoe	PH-Campbell	PH-Miller	Holt	Articles
The fossil record supports the evolution of dinosaurs into birds.	377–378	562, 566, T346	432, 807, T807	721	2:5, 3:24, 3:35, 4:17
Many major extinction events have occurred in earth's history. Some were caused by meteorite collisions.	378	340, T526, 562	431–432, 435, 799, T799	T262, 263, 392, 723, 724	2:5, 4:18, 4:19
The continents were once connected and have drifted apart over hundreds of millions of years.	378–379	322, 339, T339	T431, 832	268, 722	4:20

Note: Page numbers preceded by "T" indicate items from the teacher notes found in the margins of the Teacher's Edition.

What We Really Know about the Geologic Record

It is commonly asserted that the fossil record provides the best evidence for evolution happening on the earth. It is important to remember that the geologic evidence is the same for everyone—it is the interpretation that differs. The fossil record is no different. The evidence exists in the present, and the interpretations are about the past. No fossil, rock layer, or dating method can ever prove that evolution did, or did not, happen. The same is true for creation. Recall the distinction made between operational and historical science in Chapter 1. The presuppositions used to interpret the evidence will affect the conclusions. The fossil record must be interpreted; it cannot speak for itself.

A belief in the story of geologic time is a fundamental idea in all evolutionary contexts. If the vast expanse of time suggested by uniformitarian geology did not occur, evolution could not have occurred.

Most people, including those with training in the sciences, are not aware of the many assumptions that radiometric dating, the geologic column, and fossil interpretation use as foundations. Biologists assume that geologists have correctly identified the age of rocks. The geologists assume that the chemists have correctly identified

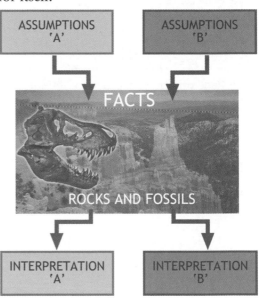

Fossils and rock layers do not speak for themselves—they must be interpreted. The way that you interpret evidence depends on the presuppositions you accept. The Bible offers a different set of presuppositions than naturalistic evolution.

the half-life of the different isotopes. Chemists assume that the physicists have correctly identified the details of radioactive decay. This chain of assumptions supporting evolution brings down the entire structure if any one of the links is weak.

The idea of geologic time was popularized by Charles Lyell in the mid-1800s. Before then, few people accepted the idea of millions of years of earth history. The development of uniformitarian thinking influenced many people in the scientific community, including Charles Darwin. This idea replaced the idea of catastrophism, a view held by biblical geologists based on the Flood and supernatural creation recorded in Genesis.

Uniformitarianism: the doctrine that present-day processes acting at similar rates as observed today account for the change evident in the geologic record.

The major problem with uniformitarianism is that it is an unverifiable assumption. There is no absolute way to measure past events. Uniformitarianism becomes a presupposition that geologic and biologic sciences are based on. Uniformitarian principles have been applied to most scientific fields, including biology, geology, nuclear physics, and astronomy. Biblical catastrophism also falls under the category of a presupposition, but it is based on God's eyewitness accounts of the Flood and creation recorded in Genesis.

Catastrophism: the doctrine that changes in the geologic record are a result of physical processes operating at rates that are dramatically higher than are observed today.

The illustrations of geologic time and the geologic column are actually composites compiled from many different sources. The fossil and geologic evidences are pieced together from all over the globe. The presence of unconformities (places where there are gaps in the sequence) is explained away,

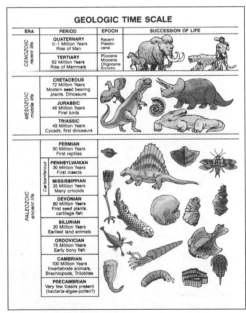

Illustrations, like this one, are actually made from combining pieces of the geologic column from all over the world. Geologists make many assumptions when trying to explain all of the fossils and rock layers.

Glencoe 372

Figure 14.2
Most sedimentary rocks form in primarily horizontal layers with the younger layers closer to the surface. Older rocks and fossils will be found deeper in the sequence, with the oldest at the bottom. **Infer** *What might have happened to a section with the oldest fossils at the top of the sequence?*

This illustration offers a false picture of what the geologic record actually looks like. The layering of fossils is not as neat and tidy as the illustration suggests. The many gaps and out-of-sequence layers suggest that the layers and fossils did not form in the way evolution suggests. Instead of challenging the underlying presupposition of gradual formation of the rock layers, the interpretation within the uniformitarian framework is adjusted. The assumption of the age of the fossils is not questioned in evolutionary thinking.

and the fact that many "ancestral" species occur higher in the strata than their descendants is ignored in these simplified illustrations. The reliability of the geologic and fossil record is summarized candidly in the quote below.

> Structure, metamorphism, sedimentary reworking and other complications have to be considered. Radiometric dating would not have been feasible if the geologic column had not been erected first. The axiom that no process can measure itself means that there is no absolute time, but this relic of the traditional mechanics persists in the common distinction between "relative" and "absolute" age.
> —D'Rourke, J. E., Pragmatism vs. materialism in stratigraphy, *American Journal of Science* **276:**54, 1976

Relative ages are assigned to rocks based on the idea that rock layers that are lower in the strata were deposited before rock layers that are higher. Creationists do not necessarily disagree with this concept, but it can only be applied to layers that are found in one location and are continuous. Determining the relative age of a rock layer is based on the assumption that you know the ages of the rocks surrounding it. Uniformitarian geologists use so-called absolute dating methods to determine the ages of the surrounding rocks.

Certain types of rocks, especially those that form from magma (igneous), contain radioactive isotopes of different elements. It is possible to measure the ratio of the different radioactive isotopes in a rock, but the ratios are not dates or ages. The dates must be inferred based on assumptions about the ratios. Some of the common isotope pairs used are K-Ar, Rb-Sr, Pb-Pb, and U-Pb. Carbon-14 dating is another common technique, but it can only be used on things that were once alive. The method of calculating radiometric dates is like using an hourglass. You can use the hourglass to tell time if you know several things: the amount of sand in the top of the hourglass when it started flowing, the rate that the sand flows through the hole in the middle, and that the quantity of sand in each chamber has not been tampered with. If any of these three conditions are not accurately known, the hourglass will give an inaccurate measure of time.

Radiometric dating is based on the fact that radioactive isotopes decay to form isotopes of different elements. The starting isotope is called the parent and the ending is called the daughter. The time it takes for one half of the parent atoms to decay to the daughter atoms is called the half-life. If certain things are known, it is possible to calculate the amount of time since the parent isotope began to decay. For example, if you began with 1 gram of Carbon-14, after 5,730 years you would be left with 0.50 g and only 0.25 g after 11,460 years. The reason this age may not be a true age—even though it is commonly called an absolute age—is that it is based on several crucial assumptions. Most radiometric dating techniques must make three assumptions:

1. The rate of radioactive decay is known and has been constant since the rock formed.

2. There has been no loss or gain of the parent or daughter isotopes from the rock.

3. The amounts of parent and daughter isotopes present when the rock formed are known.

The major problem with the first assumption is that there is no way to prove that the decay rate was not different at some point in the past. The "fact" that decay rates have always been constant is actually an inference based on a uniformitarian assumption. It is true that radioisotope decay rates are not largely affected by external conditions like change in temperature and pressure. Recent research by a creation science group known as RATE (Radioisotopes and the Age of The Earth) has produced evidence of an accelerated rate of decay at some point in the past. Creation scientists suggest that there are two possible times that God supernaturally intervened on a global scale—during Creation Week and the Flood. It is not unreasonable to assume that God used the energy of accelerated radioactive decay to initiate and drive the major geologic changes in the earth that accompanied the Flood.

The assumption that there has been no loss or gain of the isotopes in the rock (assumption 2) does not take into account the impact of weathering by water and the diffusion of gases. It is impossible to know to what degree the parent and daughter products have been added to or removed from the rocks over the alleged millions or billions of years.

The final assumption (assumption 3) does not take into account the fact that isotopes can be inherited from surrounding rock as the magma passes through the mantle and crust of the earth. Uniformitarian geologists do make efforts to eliminate errors, but the fact that rocks of known recent age give dates of millions of years supports the claim that radiometric dating cannot provide accurate "absolute" dates. Also, samples taken a few feet apart can give ages that differ by hundreds of millions of years.

Some people do not realize that fossils themselves are usually not directly dated. Instead, layers that contain datable igneous rocks above or below a fossil are used to estimate the age of the fossil. The age of the fossil can be estimated within the range of the layers above and below it. In some cases the ages are correlated to other rock layers of supposedly known age or by using index fossils. These methods assume that the distribution of index fossils and the correlation of strata are well understood on a global scale.

Evolutionists believe that a progression through the history of life can be

Fossils do not come with an age stamped on them. The dates must be interpreted from the evidence. Creationists interpret the evidence in light of the Bible and suggest that most fossils are a result of Noah's Flood. Evolution denies the authority of the Bible and uses uniformitarian thinking to interpret the evidence.

seen as you move up the geologic layers. Since the rock layers are assumed to have been laid down over billions of years, the rocks at the bottom should have the simplest forms of life, and those at the top should have more advanced forms of life. Darwin realized that if his theory were true a large number of transitional fossils would be found in the fossil record. The lack of these transitional fossils was one of the points on which Darwin said his theory would be falsified.

The lack of transitional fossils is most obvious in the rock layers from what is known as the Cambrian Period. The majority of basic multicellular body plans appear very abruptly in what is called the "Cambrian explosion." In this layer of rocks, we see an amazing array of living things that are supposed to have evolved from previous organisms. The problem is that the transitional fossils are nowhere to be found in the lower rock layers. Instead of questioning evolutionary ideas in light of this evidence, evolutionists assert that the organisms were just not fossilized or that we haven't found them yet. Creationists interpret this abrupt appearance of life in the rock record as support for the catastrophic Flood. Other theories, like saltation and punctuated equilibrium, were proposed to describe the "jerky" nature of the fossil record. Whatever the explanation, it is clear that the fossil record is not the tightly bound case for molecules-to-man evolution that evolutionists make it out to be.

The geologic layers, plate tectonics, radiometric dating, and the fossil record can all be explained within the framework provided by the Bible. Starting from the Bible—instead of naturalism—the layers of rock all over the world with billions of dead things in them are the result of the worldwide Flood described in Genesis. Although much work remains to determine the details of how the plates moved and which strata were deposited during which stages of the Flood, the overall model offers a great deal of explanatory power. Starting with the Bible as truth will lead to a much better explanation than starting with the faulty assumptions of man.

Reference Articles

4:1 The clock in the rock, www.answersingenesis.org/creation/v19/i3/clock.asp

We have all been so thoroughly soaked in the long-age thinking of our culture that most people assume that it invariably takes millions of years for sediments (like mud or sand) to harden into rock. In reality, though, all it takes is an appropriate mix of ingredients—concrete is an obvious example of rock forming quickly.

The item shown in the photograph here is a striking example of the fact that rock can form quickly. It shows part of the mechanism of a man-made clock encased in solid rock, along with seashells. Obviously, the clock was not made millions of years ago! This "clock rock" was found just a short way south of the South Jetty at Westport,

This clock encased in rock is an example of the rapid formation of rock—a process that does not take long periods of time.

Washington, USA, where there have been many shipwrecks and boats sunk in the area.

4:2 Fascinating fossil fence-wire, www.answersingenesis.org/creation/v20/i3/fossil.asp

A young girl found a large circular object on a beach in Australia. The object turned out to be a roll of fence wire that had become entirely encased in sand and shells. The iron oxide compounds acted to cement the particles together and form a mass of solid rock in a matter of decades. Unfortunately, the average person is still conditioned into thinking millions of years when considering how rocks and fossils form. But as we've said many times with many examples—given the right conditions, rocks and fossils will form in a very short time.

4:3 Can Flood geology explain thick chalk beds? Snelling, www. answersingenesis.org/tj/v8/i1/chalk.asp

Chalk deposits are the calcite remaining from the shells of microorganisms: foraminifera and coccolithophores. Evolutionists argue that the Flood model does not allow for the thick layers of chalk found all over the world. Uniformitarian geologists assume that the chalk layers form as the shells of these dead microorganisms fall to the ocean floor and slowly build up. Calculations done by Dr. Ariel Roth suggest that the rate of formation of the chalk layers is not a problem in the time span before the Flood. John Woodmorappe took the 17.5 million cubic kilometers of limestone and chalk that exist in the same layers as chalk beds and calculated that only 4.1% of the earth's surface would need to be covered with the microorganisms to form the rocks.

The problem is not only how much chalk could have been formed but when it was formed. The chalk deposits sit in a layer that is thought to have been formed during the Flood. The conditions during the Flood (warm water, wind, upwelling, nutrient flow from the land, and decaying animals) would have been ideal for the microorganisms and could have caused a bloom in the populations. Under these conditions, the organisms needed for chalk formation could have grown quite rapidly. The purity of the chalk beds is another testament to the rapid nature with which they formed, a fact that evolutionists have a hard time explaining away. The biblical Flood offers a reasonable explanation for the formation of the thick, pure chalk layers seen around the world.

4:4 Fossils—do they get more complex? www.answersingenesis. org/creation/v20/i2/fossils.asp

Evolutionary theory would predict that organisms lower in the geologic strata would be less complex than those in higher layers. When evolutionists looked at ammonite shells and descendant-ancestor pairs of vertebrates, no trend in increasing complexity was found.

Analyzing Information   **PH-Campbell 351**

18. **Analyzing Diagrams** Use the diagram of sedimentary rock layers below to answer the questions.

a. What major change in the environment occurred after layers D and E? Explain.
b. What inferences can you make about life forms at the time layer A was formed?
c. If radiometric dating identifies the rock in layer C as 425 million years old, what can you infer about the age of the fossils in layer C? In layers B and D? Explain.

The fact that the illustration shows increasing complexity in higher strata does not mean that evolution has occurred. Evolution predicts a gradual series of complexity within a group. The gradual changes of evolutionary history (i.e., simple reptile to complex reptile) are not found in the fossil record. In many cases, the evolutionary "ancestor" is found in higher strata.

4:5 The fossils say what? Ham, www.answersingenesis.org/creation/v4/i4/fossils.asp

Most evolutionists have abandoned the idea that humans are the pinnacle of evolution; bacteria have been evolving just as long as humans have. No organism can be considered more evolved than another—evolution is not an upward or goal-directed process. Using this concept, man is no more important than cows or mosquitoes. This runs contrary to the Bible's teaching that man was made in the image of God. Evolution offers man "freedom" from right and wrong, while the Creator God demands accountability from his creation.

4:6 Dinosaur soft parts, Morris, www.icr.org/article/2032

The discovery of a *T. rex* bone that contained soft tissues has forced evolutionists to reconsider their ideas about fossilization. The bone, which is allegedly 70 million years old, was found in porous sandstone that should have allowed the bone to fill with mineral deposits. The fact that the bone was still "fresh" does not prove it is young, but it

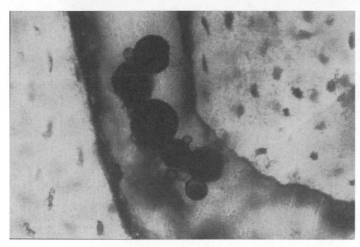

The presence of soft tissue structures found in dinosaur fossils makes it clear that they are not 70 million years old.

does challenge the validity of the 70 million year old date. Any biological material should have broken down in that time. It even stretches the limits of the creationist date of fewer than 5,000 years.

Secular scientists deny the possibility that the age is wrong and are trying to explain the amazing preservation through natural processes.

4:7 Focus: Ancient organisms stay the same, www.answersingenesis.org/creation/v21/i3/news.asp

A while ago, evolutionists would not have expected to find any fossils in rocks that they thought were, say, three billion years old—life supposedly hadn't evolved yet. However, fossils of bacteria kept turning up in progressively "older" rocks (no surprise to creationists), which allowed less and less time for the first life to evolve in the hypothetical, oxygen-free "early atmosphere." Now an Austrian/Swiss team of scientists has looked at rock from Western Australia's Pilbara region, supposedly around 3.5 billion years old, and found fossilized cyanobacteria. These appear to be indistinguishable from the same (oxygen-producing) creatures making the mat structures called stromatolites in the shallows of Shark Bay, some 500 kilometers away on the coast.

4:8 Focus: Rocks forming in months, www.answersingenesis.org/creation/v17/i2/focus.asp

Stones measuring up to a foot across are forming in a Norfolk (UK) marsh in a process which is happening in a few months or years. Small (and not so small) black lumps of rock are forming, as bacteria thriving on rotting vegetation produce "an iron-rich form of limestone, which acts as a mineral cement, binding the sand and mud together." Geologists have dug up similar stones before, which "often contain beautifully formed fossils." These fossils show a lot of detail of the soft flesh, "as it had no time to rot before the rock formed around it." Geology Professor Max Coleman, who works for BP, is keen to study the marsh. The rock is "forming faster than anyone had ever believed possible, with one stone creating itself in just six months" (*Eastern Daily Press*, UK, October 5, 1994). Creationists have long pointed out that hardening of sediments into rock is mainly a matter of the right cementing substances being present and that it doesn't require millions of years.

4:9 Rodent Resurrected? www.answersingenesis.org/articles/am/v1/n1/rodent-resurrected#fnList_1_2

In the evolutionary scenario, when an animal or plant has gone "extinct," and then is found living today, unchanged from what is found in the fossil record, this shocking discovery is called a "living fossil."

A recent example is a rodent that was found in Southeast Asia. It was identified as one of a group of mammals called *diatonyids*, which were thought by evolutionists to have gone

The presence of "living fossils" like this coelacanth casts doubt on the value of evolution as a predictive model—organisms can change rapidly or stay the same for hundreds of millions of years. Other examples of living fossils include wasps, dragonflies, stromatolites, Ginkgo, clams, and the Wollemi pine.

extinct about 11 million years ago. Of course, it is now obvious that this animal never was extinct. Because Noah's Flood occurred about 4,400 years ago, it is not a surprise among creationists that this "extinct" rodent is the same in the fossil record as what has been rediscovered today. But it is a major problem for evolutionists because this rodent has somehow "forgotten" to evolve over millions of years.

The obvious interpretation, as you look at the creature preserved in the fossil record (which creationists argue is largely the result of the Flood) and compare it to today's animal, is that it has remained the same. This "new" rodent fits well with the creation model, but certainly not with the evolutionary one.

4:10 Rock Layers Folded, Not Fractured, Snelling, www.answersingenesis.org/articles/am/v4/n2/folded-not-fractured

The fossil-bearing geologic record consists of tens of thousands of feet of sedimentary layers, though not all these layers are found everywhere around the globe, and their thickness varies from place to place. At most locations only a small portion is available to view, such as about 4,500 feet (1371 m) of strata in the walls of Grand Canyon.

Uniformitarian (long-age) geologists believe that these sedimentary layers were sporadically deposited and deformed over the past 500 million years. In contrast, if the global cataclysmic Genesis Flood deposited all these strata

Uniformitarian thinking says that most canyons form from a little water over a long period of time. Catastrophism explains canyon formation from a lot of water over a short time. Canyons near Mount St. Helens and the scablands of eastern Washington provide evidence of canyon formation in a matter of days.

GOD'S WORD IS TRUTH

MAN DECIDES TRUTH

in a little more than a year, then the individual layers would have been deposited in rapid succession, one on top of the other. If the lower rock layers were deposited millions of years before the upper layers, they would be hard and brittle. Large sections of the rock sequence near Grand Canyon are bent in a way that cannot be explained by gradual processes acting on solid rock. The biblical explanation of rapid deposition of the layers and deforming them before they had completely solidified explains the folding seen. The millions of years supposedly recorded in the layers of the canyon are imaginary.

4:11 A canyon in six days! Morris, www.answersingenesis.org/go/walla-canyon

Most people are taught that Grand Canyon formed as the Colorado River eroded the landscape over tens of millions of years. The fact that the same results could be accomplished with a lot of water over a short time is generally not mentioned. Observations of canyon formation in modern times suggest that Grand Canyon may have formed much as did a small canyon near Walla Walla, Washington—a lot of water over a short time. During an unusually wet period, a small irrigation ditch was used to divert some excess water. As the water passed through the ditch, it became a gully, then a gulch, then a canyon, 1,500 feet long and 120 feet deep. This all happened in six days, not millions of years. The similar formation of the Toutle River canyon near Mount St. Helens offers another example that is analogous to what would have happened as the floodwaters receded in the days of Noah.

4:12 *National Geographic* plays the dating game, Woodmorappe, www.answersingenesis.org/tj/v16/i1/dating_game.asp

National Geographic magazine is known for its amazing photography and cultural coverage, as well as its evolutionary support. In an article on radiometric dating, the many assumptions that must be made to arrive at dates of millions of years were not discussed. This failure to discuss the underlying assumptions leaves the layperson thinking that determining the age of rocks is a fool-proof science. The article uses the Hubble constant to establish an old age of the universe without mentioning the many problems with big bang cosmology. The oldest rocks on earth are said to be 4.03 billion years even though rocks dating 10 billion years old have been recorded. The rate of radioactive decay is assumed to be constant throughout history, even though this cannot be proven. Several evidences in the RATE project seem to support the idea that the rate of radioactive decay has not always been constant.

All dating methods assume that the rock is a closed system where none of the parent or daughter isotopes can enter or leave. The assumption that dates are accurate if they are consistent across methods, known as isochrons, is based on assumptions, and the majority of dates are not consistent for a given rock. Geologists generally do not test more than a few methods on a limited number of samples, and when they return "impossible" dates, they are rejected completely. When many dates are returned for a sample, the "proper" date is selected to fit the expected age. The presence of wood in a lava flow that was dated millions of years younger than the rock (and lower strata dating much younger than higher strata) call the assumptions into question. Samples from lava flows of known age regularly return ages of millions of years instead of the actual age. The many assumptions involved in radiometric dating, coupled with the unreliable nature of the dates, calls into question the results of radiometric dating.

4:13 How well do paleontologists know fossil distributions?
Oard, www.answersingenesis.org/tj/v14/i1/fossils.asp

Scientists often use the presence of index fossils to estimate how old a given layer of rock is. The problem is that many virtually identical specimens are found in different geologic layers and separated from one another. Based on the standard uniformitarian assumptions, these specimens are given different names. This overstates the actual number of species found in the fossil record and confuses their distribution. There are often large gaps of missing time between the two specimens. Evolutionists have trouble explaining why the species is not found in the layers between the two fossil specimens, but creationists have no difficulty. The Flood model explains the wide distribution and the different levels as the organisms were buried in different places during the same Flood event. The actual three-dimensional distributions of fossil species is not known by paleontologists, but it is used to prove that evolution and evolutionary time are true.

4:14 Ten misconceptions about the geologic column, www.icr.org/article/242/107/

This article presents ten misconceptions about the geologic column, discussing the composition of the column, its correlation to the age of the earth, and the dating of layers from fossils and other uniformitarian assumptions. Some selected examples are discussed here.

The geologic column was actually constructed based on empirical evidence from the rock record by men who would be called progressive creationists in today's terms. The geologic time periods and eras were added later by uniformitarian scientists.

The geologic record for any given area is not always consistent with the geologic column shown in textbooks. The layers are sometimes out of order or absent which can make identifying the layers difficult. Using index fossils to correlate rock layers across continents is not always reliable, but data from drilling, seismic activity, and surface features allow many layers to be correlated across continents.

Radiometric dating often gives discordant ages to rock layers, and the process of sedimentation does not require millions of years. Connected to this idea are the illustrations of the geologic ages with their built-in evolutionary bias. However, these are just representations of what these sedimentary environments may have looked like and do not necessarily support the supposed evolutionary story they are supposed to represent.

4:15 Radioisotopes and the age of the earth, Snelling, www.answersingenesis.org/articles/am/v2/n4/radioisotopes-earth

A long-term research project involving several creation scientists has produced intriguing new evidence in support of an earth that is thousands of years old rather than many billions. Some of the findings are summarized below.

The presence of fission tracks and radiohalos in crystals demonstrates that hundreds of millions of years worth of radioactive decay has occurred in a very short period. Because the Bible indicates the earth is young (about 6,000 years old), this large quantity of nuclear decay must have occurred at much faster rates than those measured today.

Using various radiometric dating methods to measure the ages of rock samples consistently produced ages that varied greatly. This may be explained by the different parent atoms having decayed at different rates in the past—an explanation not allowed by evolutionists. These changes in decay rates could be accounted for by very small changes in the binding forces within the nuclei of the parent atoms.

Research has been done to demonstrate that many of the assumptions used in radiometric dating are false. Starting from biblical assumptions regarding the Flood and Creation can provide a new framework for interpreting current scientific data.

4:16 What grows on evolution's tree? Morris, www.icr.org/article/577

Evolutionists use the concept of the tree of life to show how all life on earth originated with a single common ancestor. The evidence for the branching tree cannot be found in the fossil record where there are many gaps and reversals. Textbooks present this tree as fact and the evolutionary indoctrination continues. The falsity of the tree is most evident in the "Cambrian explosion." In these rock layers the majority of body plans (phyla) appear completely formed without evidence of their ancestry in the layers below. There have been no new phyla since the Cambrian Period when they all appear suddenly. The fossil record stands as a firm testimony to the creation of life, not its evolution by natural processes.

4:17 Claws on wings, www.answersingenesis.org/creation/v5/i2/claws.asp

Many people have tried to say that the proof that reptiles evolved into birds is to be found in a fossil bird called *Archaeopteryx*, which shows claws on its fossilized feathered wings. But all the living birds with claws on their wings are obviously birds! *Archaeopteryx* and the living "clawed" birds tell us only that some kinds of birds have wing claws and some don't. Such

The fact that *Archaeopteryx* has reptilian characteristics does not mean that it is not a bird. Several living birds, like the hoatzin, have claws on their wings like *Archaeopteryx*. Experts generally agree that *Archaeopteryx* is a bird, not a transitional form.

claws are not something new in birds, and they certainly don't show that birds with them are any more reptile-like than birds without such claws.

4:18 The Permian extinction: *National Geographic* **comes close to the truth,** Silvestru, www.answersingenesis.org/tj/v15/i1/permian.asp

Evolutionists believe that a mass extinction, wiping out 90% of the planet's species, occurred about 250 million years ago. The presence of 9 major extinctions has led to much speculation about the cause. Some suggested causes of the Permian extinction are major asteroid impacts, increased volcanism, and depleted oxygen in the oceans. The asteroid impact supposedly caused major dust clouds that led to the collapse of food chains and eventually acute global warming, which wiped out most species. The theory using ocean oxygen levels is unsupported by real evidence.

There is a large amount of volcanic activity in Siberia at this point in the strata, and some argue the asteroid evidence is better explained by these volcanoes. The same sort of sun-blocking chain reaction would result from massive volcanic activity.

Creationists explain the apparent mass extinctions as distinct events or zones within the year of the Flood. The idea of asteroid impacts as a trigger for the Catastrophic Plate Tectonics Model developed by Dr. John Baumgardner is an interesting idea. The idea of a lot of small catastrophes over millions of years can all be encapsulated into the 371-day Flood. The evidence for a global flood is misinterpreted by the uniformitarian geologists.

4:19 The extinction of the dinosaurs, Oard, www.answersingenesis.org/tj/v11/i2/dinosaur.asp

The disappearance of dinosaurs from the earth in a relatively short time has been a major puzzle for evolutionists. Their wide distribution and adaptation to many climates deepens the mystery. Studying extinctions is difficult because the classification and distribution of species is not well described. Up to nine major extinction events are supposedly preserved in the fossil record, the one at the end of the Cretaceous being the most extensive.

Different theories on extinction range from one extreme to the other, including temperature, nutrition, and food supply. Lately, the meteorite extinction theory seems to be the most prevalent. A massive meteorite struck the earth, ejecting debris into the air that cooled the atmosphere. A layer of iridium concentration around the globe, the presence of shocked quartz, and many other types of evidence are supposed support for the theory. The cooling from the debris is alleged to have caused the extinction of the dinosaurs.

A competing theory suggests that the data supports a period of massive volcanic activity. Many types of evidence, including the iridium and quartz evidence, are given as support for the theory. The increased volcanic

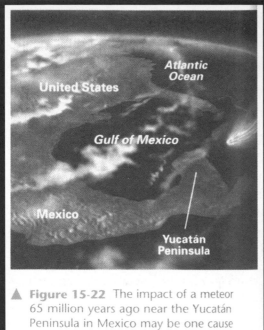

Many people believe that one or more of the major extinction events in evolutionary history occurred as a result of a meteorite hitting the earth. In the picture here, the meteorite that is alleged to have hit in the Yucatan area is depicted. The creation model uses the Genesis Flood to explain the sudden disappearance of the majority of life on earth and the presence of billions of fossils buried in rock layers laid down by water.

▲ **Figure 15-22** The impact of a meteor 65 million years ago near the Yucatán Peninsula in Mexico may be one cause of the extinction of many land plants and animals in North America.

PH-Campbell 340

activity would have caused the same cooling effect, as well as releasing toxic gases and killing the dinosaurs. Opponents of each theory have valid arguments to refute one another.

Creationists hold that the destruction of most of the dinosaurs, as well as most other life forms, is accounted for by Noah's Flood. Those dinosaurs that survived the Flood in the Ark have died off since then for various reasons. While there are still many unknowns in the fossil distribution, the presence of massive fossil graveyards, trackways that represent fleeing behavior, quickly deposited layers without channels forming, and other factors clearly point to a flood of global proportions. There are certain aspects of Flood geology that are not entirely understood, but the models are constantly being refined to accommodate these observations. The likelihood of volcanoes and/or meteorite collisions during the Flood explains the evidence for the two most popular secular theories adequately. In total, the

Genesis Flood provides a satisfactory explanation for the extinction of a majority of the dinosaurs.

4:20 Can catastrophic plate tectonics explain flood geology?
Snelling, www.answersingenesis.org/articles/nab/catastrophic-plate-tectonics

The study of plate tectonics is an interpretation or model of how the plates of the earth have moved in the past. The earth's crust is made of plates of different types of rock. Continental plates are made of granites and sedimentary rocks and the ocean plates are made of basalt. All of these plates float on the mantle below. Plates can be deformed by rifting, faulting, compressing, and subducting under another plate. Rifting occurs when plates move apart, such as along the Mid-Atlantic Ridge and the East African Rift. Transform faulting happens when plates slide horizontally past one another in places such as along the San Andreas Fault. Compression occurs when plates move toward one another. Ocean plates will plunge below continental plates, but continental plates collide to form mountains like the Himalayas.

In 1859 Antonio Snider used Genesis 1:9–10 and the close fit of western Africa and eastern South America to suggest that a supercontinent split apart catastrophically during the Flood. Over time, the continents moved into their present positions. His theory was unnoticed, and the theory of continental drift was later proposed by Alfred Wegener. His theory was spurned for 50 years by most geologists, and it was called pseudo-scientific fantasy that violated basic principles of physics. Today, plate tectonics involving continental drift is the ruling perspective.

The mapping of the seafloor, measurement of the seafloor's magnetic field directions, radiometric dating, and detection of earthquakes using seismometers all led to an acceptance of the theory. The correlation of fossils across ocean basins, the pattern of seafloor magnetic reversals, and the locations of earthquakes and mountains, along with other evidence, were also elegantly explained by the theory.

Uniformitarian geologists take the vast ages for granted when describing continental drift. Assuming that the rate we see today has been constant, the continents must have been moving for hundreds of millions of years. However, many observations suggest a rapid movement. The seafloor surface appears to have a smooth zebra-striped magnetic pattern, but drilling into the basalts reveals past rapid and erratic changes. This is consistent with the rapid extrusion of the basalts and rapid magnetic reversals during the Flood. The lack of compressional features in ocean trench sediments also points to their rapid deposition at the end of the Flood.

Snider's original proposal of continental sprint, rather than the uniformitarian idea of continental drift, has been supported by computer modeling and explains the evidence better. The catastrophic plate tectonics model begins with a pre-Flood supercontinent, Rodinia. Some sudden trigger cracked the ocean floors next to this cold continent. This caused large blocks to move down into the mantle pulling the ocean floor with them, triggering a runaway subduction event that replaced the entire ocean floor in a matter of weeks. As the crust sank, the mantle rock was displaced and rose along rift zones within the oceans, creating new sea floor.

As this hot magma encountered the ocean waters, great jets of steam were produced, perhaps explaining the "fountains of the great deep" described in Genesis 7:11 and 8:2. This would have caused global rainfall for the duration of the 40 days and nights described in Genesis. The new, hot ocean floor would float higher than the old, cold floor and cause the ocean basins to rise, displacing their waters to flood over the continents. This explains why vast layers of sedimentary rocks containing marine creatures are spread across the continents, something slow-and-gradual processes cannot explain. The rapid replacement of the ocean floor would account for the erratic magnetic reversals recorded in the rocks.

Once the old ocean floor had been subducted, the process slowed and the new ocean floor rocks cooled. As they cooled, they would become less dense and sink, allowing the water to flow off of the continents and into the new deeper ocean basins. The continents would have risen including the newly formed mountains that resulted from the collisions of the plates during the Flood. The gradual rates of current plate movement could not have provided enough force to create mountains, but the catastrophic collision in a runaway model would rapidly buckle the strata and push up high mountains.

Plate tectonics is not directly mentioned in the Bible, but Genesis 1:9–10 suggests that all of the land was once connected, whereas the continents are now separated. The catastrophic plate tectonics model and continental sprint during the Flood can explain this. The model also explains, in a consistent manner, the global flooding and rain described in Genesis. Starting with the Bible, an explanation for the global Flood and the movements of the continents can be provided within the biblical time frame—not billions of years.

Questions to Consider

1. How are polystrate fossils, like upright trees, explained if each of the layers surrounding the fossil takes long periods of time to form? Wouldn't the wood rot away before it was covered?

2. Do radiometric dating techniques always show that rocks lower in the geologic layers are older than rocks that are higher?

3. If radiometric dating on rocks known to be only a few years old yields dates of hundreds of millions of years, why should we trust that the techniques can be used to accurately date rocks of unknown ages?

4. Don't large fossil graveyards suggest a major catastrophe? Could a massive flood explain these deposits?

5. How could large fossil graveyards be explained without a massive catastrophe?

6. How soon after death would a large dinosaur (or a group of large dinosaurs) need to be buried by sediment to prevent scavengers from scattering its bones? It would seem this would need to be a catastrophic event to bury this large animal in sediment.

7. How do artists decide what an extinct organism should look like? Would a camel skeleton indicate whether it had one or more humps?

8. If you gave the same hominid bones to four different artists, would they draw the same picture of the creature? Why should we trust, or even use, artists' representations in science? (See Behind the Scenes, *National Geographic,* March 2000, p. 140 for an article on *Homo habilis* fossil drawings.)

9. If the Cambrian explosion happened because of empty ecological niches, why didn't similar events occur after later extinction episodes?

10. In radiometric dating techniques, how do we know how much parent material the sample started with? How do we know none of the parent or daughter isotope was added or removed? How do we know the decay rate is constant?

11. When items are carbon-14 dated, how do we know how much carbon-14 was initially present in the sample? Could the ratio of carbon-12 to carbon-14 have been different at different times in earth's history? How can scientists accurately adjust their calculations if the isotope ratios were never observed and recorded?

Tools for Digging Deeper

(see a complete list in the Introduction)

The New Answers Book 1 & 2 by Ham et al.

Creation: Facts of Life by Gary Parker

Evolution: The Fossils Still Say No! by Duane Gish

The Fossil Book by Gary Parker

The Geology Book by John Morris

www.answersingenesis.org/go/geology

www.answersingenesis.org/go/fossils

05

Research on the origin of life seems to be unique in that the conclusion has already been authoritatively accepted ... . What remains to be done is to find the scenarios which describe the detailed mechanisms and processes by which this happened. One must conclude that, contrary to the established and current wisdom, a scenario describing the genesis of life on earth by chance and natural causes which can be accepted on the basis of fact and not faith has not yet been written.

–Yockey, H.P., A calculation of the probability of spontaneous biogenesis by information theory, *Journal of Theoretical Biology* **67:**377–398, 1977

What You Will Learn

The naturalistic philosophy of modern science has created a dilemma for evolution. No known laws of nature allow complex, living, information-containing systems to develop from the random interactions of matter. Yet, this is what is required in order for life to have evolved in the universe. Creationists accept that life appeared on earth as a direct creative act of God. The design and information that we see in all living things is a result of an intelligence—not random occurrences. Many biologists try to separate the origin of life (sometimes called chemical evolution) and the universe from discussions of biology. These scientists recognize the challenge presented by chemical evolution, but their commitment to naturalism leaves them no other choice. Many different models are used to explain how life can come from nonliving matter, but all of these models, including the famous Miller-Urey experiment, fail to account for the many chemical and biological barriers to spontaneously forming life.

In the face of the challenges to chemical evolution, one of the codiscoverers of DNA has proposed that life was actually "seeded" by some alien intelligence. This does not solve the problem but only pushes the origin of life problem to another place. It also takes the issue out of the scope of science—such a hypothesis cannot be tested, it must be accepted on faith. The failure of science to demonstrate how, where, when, or why life was naturally formed makes the acceptance of chemical evolution a matter of faith. Other attempts to explain how life formed are riddled with "maybe" and "possibly." It requires more faith to believe that the universe and all of the living things on earth came from a big bang than it does to accept that the design we see must have had a Designer. God has revealed how life began on earth—He spoke it into existence.

What Your Textbook Says about the Origin of Life

Evolutionary Concept	Glencoe	PH-Campbell	PH-Miller	Holt	Articles
The earth formed 4.6 billion years ago, and life first appeared about 3.9 billion years ago.	369	356	424	252	5:1, 5:5
Chemicals present on the early earth assembled themselves to form cells. The scientific method can help us understand how this happened.	368, 381, 383	356–357, T357, 359, 366	386, 423–424, T423	34, 252–253, 256	3:2, 5:1, 5:2, 5:3, 5:5, 5:6
The properties of water and the characteristics of earth are ideal for life. Other planets in the universe may have evolved life as well.	—	81–87	—	31, 254, T255, T415	3:2, 5:4
Cell Theory: All cells come from preexisting cells.	172, 203	110, 180	13–14, 170	55	5:1, 5:6
The early earth had a reducing atmosphere with little or no oxygen. Oxygen became abundant as photosynthetic bacteria evolved.	382–383	357, 366	211, 423, 426, T426	254	5:3, 5:5
The Miller experiment and others demonstrate that life could have formed in the "primordial soup."	382, 388	357, 359	423–424, T424	254, T257	5:3, 5:5, 5:6

Evolutionary Concept	Glencoe	PH-Campbell	PH-Miller	Holt	Articles
Amino acids may have assembled into proteins on clay particles in shallow pools.	383	357	T426	—	5:1, 5:2, 5:5, 5:6
Life began with RNA that acted as enzymes and information templates.	388	358	291, 293, 425	256–257, T256	3:2, 5:2, 5:5
Life on earth may have come from other planets where there is life.	388	T357, T361	—	—	3:2, 5:4
Precells (protocells) form when lipids are mixed with certain organic molecules.	383	358	425	256–257	3:2, 5:5
Life may have originated in deep-sea thermal vents or bubbles in the ocean.	—	359	—	254–255	3:2, 5:5, 5:6

Note: Page numbers preceded by "T" indicate items from the teacher notes found in the margins of the Teacher's Edition.

What We Really Know about the Origin of Life

Research on how life first arose from inanimate matter is an example of historical science at its worst. There is absolutely no way to verify any hypothesis that attempts to explain how the very first living thing came about in a purely naturalistic way. Some evolutionary biologists try to separate the origin of life issue from evolutionary biology. The problem with this is that evolutionary scientists have a commitment to naturalism—all phenomena must be explained using only natural laws. Since the appearance of life on earth is a phenomenon that occurred, it must be explained. Naturalists must follow an evolutionary chain from the organisms living today back to the beginning of the universe. For them, complex animals came from simple animals which came from simpler organisms which came from chemicals which came from stardust. If one of these pieces is missing, evolutionary thinking loses its foundation. Naturalistic scientists often talk about evolution in more than the common biological sense—chemical/organic evolution and the evolution of the universe from the big bang often appear in biology textbooks despite attempts to separate the issues.

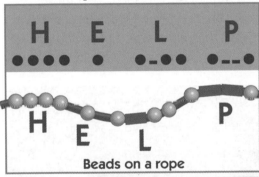

Beads on a rope

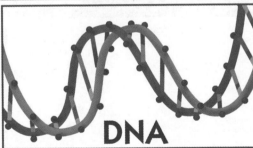

DNA

DNA contains information coded in the sequence of base pairs. The information can be compared to other forms of information like Morse code. There are no known natural laws that explain how information can arise from the random interactions of matter. The origin of information cannot be explained by evolution.

What if a scientist could make a living organism by combining chemicals in a lab? It would only prove that intelligent actions can make life—not that life arose spontaneously billions of years ago. There has never been an instance where information has been shown to arise from matter. Matter can form complex patterns, such as crystals, but there is no information contained in such patterns. In order for life to continue and organisms to replicate, information must be present to pass on to offspring. The ultimate question that evolution must be able to answer is, "How did the information seen in living things arise from matter alone?" When we think of information in biology, we are mainly talking about DNA and RNA. DNA and RNA use information that is present in a code to send and receive messages that are intended to produce proteins and continue the existence of the species. We can define information as follows:

Information: an encoded, symbolically represented message conveying expected action and intended purpose.

One of the pioneering ideas in organic evolution was the "primordial soup." According to this model, at some point in earth history, the molten earth cooled and oceans formed. As rain fell, chemicals in a hypothetical pool, warmed by the volcanic activity and energized by lightning, organized into proteins, lipids, and carbohydrates. These molecules then organized into cellular structures

Miller's experiment demonstrates that intelligence can create some of the components of life. Most textbooks do not report the fact that Miller's environmental conditions are not accepted any longer. Miller's experiment produced a mixture that would have been toxic to life. The few biological chemicals that were formed had to be isolated from the watery environment, or none of them would have formed.

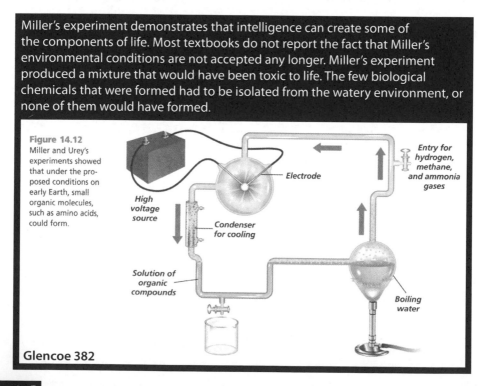

Figure 14.12
Miller and Urey's experiments showed that under the proposed conditions on early Earth, small organic molecules, such as amino acids, could form.

High voltage source

Electrode

Entry for hydrogen, methane, and ammonia gases

Condenser for cooling

Solution of organic compounds

Boiling water

Glencoe 382

like proteins, DNA, and cell membranes. The problem with this scenario is that chemistry prohibits it. Proteins do not form from piles of amino acids, and DNA contains a specific code that must be copied from another strand of DNA. Proteins cannot form in water because the water breaks the bonds that hold the amino acids together—a process called hydrolysis.

One of the most famous experiments done in the primordial soup model was performed by Stanley Miller. Miller's experiment is featured in virtually every textbook as proof that life could have come from matter. The major flaws in Miller's experiment are rarely communicated to readers, and few scientists believe the scenario is accurate. Many other models have popped up in the decades since, but none have produced any more evidence than Miller's failed explanation.

The panspermia hypothesis suggests that aliens seeded life on earth by providing the DNA (promoted by DNA codiscoverer Francis Crick and depicted in the movie *Mission to Mars*), but this is a supernatural explanation and doesn't solve the origin of life problem—where did the aliens come from?

Recently, a hypothesis involving bubbles from deep ocean vents was put forward, but the same chemistry limitations apply. One of the most recent ideas is that viruses were the first forms of life, but viruses need cells to reproduce themselves. At present, there is no consensus among evolutionary scientists as to which of these scenarios produced life from simple chemicals.

> Nobody understands the origin of life. If they say they
> do, they are probably trying to fool you.

> —Ken Nealson (University of Southern California),
> The search for the scum of the universe, www.
> space.com/scienceastronomy/astronomy/odds_of_
> et_020521-1.html

Similar to panspermia is the idea that life ought to exist on other planets in our universe. Evolutionists reason that if there are hundreds of billions of stars in our universe, at least one of those must have a planet similar to earth that could support life. If life evolved on earth, it could have evolved on other planets. Within our solar system, Jupiter's moon Europa and Mars are the focus of study. Billions of dollars are spent looking for life on other planets and listening for signals from extraterrestrials. The fact that bacteria have been found in extreme locations on earth drives evolutionists to believe they could have evolved and perhaps live in many places in the universe.

Another popular idea is that some intelligent designer created the universe and used the various types of evolution to accomplish his goals. This designer has intervened in history at various points and helped out his creation from time to time. The problem with this idea is that there is no way to tell when the designer intervened, and acceptance of this designer does not mean that the God of the Bible exists. Intelligent design, as a movement, does not recognize or promote any particular god, but accepts any. This idea may very well lead people away from the true God of the Bible by allowing them to choose whatever story they want to. The idea has been rejected by evolutionary scientists and the courts.

The only true account of the origin of life on earth is found in the account of the only Eyewitness who was there. The Bible

Many ideas have been proposed to get around the chemical problems associated with the origin of life. One model suggests that bubbles allowed the compounds to become more concentrated, but there are still many physical and chemical barriers. Some scientists have recognized the impossibility of life forming on the earth and have suggested that life came from outer space—possibly from alien life forms.

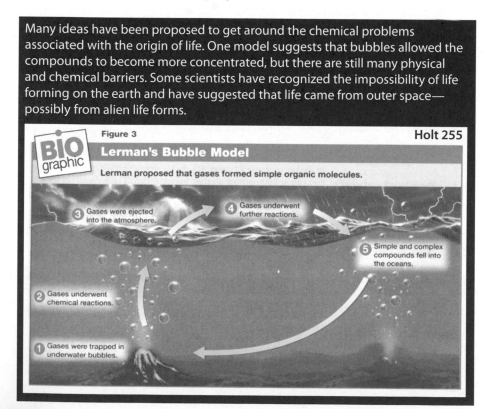

BIO graphic

Figure 3   **Holt 255**

Lerman's Bubble Model

Lerman proposed that gases formed simple organic molecules.

3 Gases were ejected into the atmosphere.

4 Gases underwent further reactions.

5 Simple and complex compounds fell into the oceans.

2 Gases underwent chemical reactions.

1 Gases were trapped in underwater bubbles.

explains that the presence of life on earth is the result of supernatural actions of an omnipotent Intelligent Designer—the God of the Bible. Many complain that accepting this supernatural explanation stops anyone from pursuing knowledge about the natural world, but the presence of a logical Creator provides a reason to look for order in the universe. This point is underscored by the fact that many of the major fields of science were founded by men who believed in the Creator God of the Bible. The only aspect of science that the acceptance of creation excludes is the story of evolution.

Reference Articles

5:1 Life from life . . . or not? Demick, www.answersingenesis.org/creation/v23/i1/life.asp

Darwin did not directly mention the idea of chemical evolution, but it is a natural extension of the logic of naturalism. Thomas Huxley, known as "Darwin's bulldog," boldly proclaimed the ability of life to come from nonlife. The idea of life coming from nonlife, spontaneous generation, was a popular idea from the time of the Greek philosophers. Louis Pasteur had performed experiments that showed spontaneous generation was not possible; so Huxley called the idea of the origin of life "abiogenesis" and said the evolution of protoplasm from nonliving matter had happened only in the early earth and could no longer be observed. This fact seems to disqualify it from scientific study. The Bible also explains that we should not expect to see life coming from nonliving matter since God ceased His creative activity after Day 6 of creation. So, evolutionists accept that spontaneous generation happened to get life started, but it can't happen today—a clearly fallacious argument that is necessary to support evolution.

Scientists tried to show that Pasteur's work was wrong, but the many practical applications of the idea forced scientists to abandon the idea of spontaneous generation. The work of Rudolf Virchow helped to confirm that all cells come from preexisting cells, not chemical imbalances. Still needing a mechanism to create life from matter, Huxley and Ernst Haeckel described a group of organisms between matter and cells. They found what they were looking for (because they had decided beforehand what it would look like), but it was later shown to be a simple mixture of chemicals and seawater. As these men were looking for the origin of life, they had no idea of the complexity of even the simplest cells. Each new discovery at the genetic and molecular level just makes it all the more evident that life did not spontaneously create itself—it had a Creator.

5:2 Evolutionist criticisms of the RNA world conjecture, Cairns-Smith, www.answersingenesis.org/home/area/tools/Quotes/cairns-smith_RNA.asp

Many of the theories on the origin of life may seem a little bizarre, but they come about when evolutionists realize the impossibility of chemical evolution producing life as we know it. One such evolutionist is Graham Cairns-Smith and his theory involving clay particles in the early earth. Cairns-Smith suggests that the many detailed experiments on the plausibility of chemical evolution have only gone to show the unlikelihood of its occurrence. It is highly unlikely that complex sugars and proteins (polysaccharides and polypeptides) could form, but even more unlikely that polynucleotides like DNA and RNA could spontaneously form. Cairns-Smith lists 19 difficulties that suggest the unlikelihood of the RNA world hypothesis and shows that the origin of life by a purely naturalistic accident is highly improbable.

5:3 Can natural processes explain the origin of life? Riddle, www.answersingenesis.org/articles/wow/can-natural-processes-explain

This chapter from *The New Answers Book 2* examines the orgin of life. Some evolutionists, realizing the improbability of the spontaneous generation of life, suggest that life started somewhere else in the universe and arrived on earth somehow. The problem with this idea is that it cannot be tested and it just pushes the problem from earth to another planet. Experiments conducted by Stanley Miller in the early 1950s produced some of the basic building blocks of life, but what conclusions can be drawn from the experiments? Relying on an intelligently designed procedure and apparatus, Miller succeeded in producing a few of the 20 amino acids found in living things. One of the major problems for the origin of life is the presence of oxygen. Oxygen would tend to destroy the organic compounds needed for life, but if oxygen were absent, the atmosphere would lack an ozone layer to shield the compounds from ultraviolet rays—a Catch-22 for evolutionists. Miller excluded oxygen from his experiment, though today the evidence points to the presence of oxygen in the atmosphere throughout earth's history. Starting in water is also a problem since water tends to break the bonds of some amino acids and prevents them from forming chains. Miller isolated the products in order to avoid this destructive reaction.

Another significant problem is that the amino acids in living things, 20 of the over 2,000 types, are found in left- and right-handed forms called "enantiomers." Miller's experiment produced a racemic mixture (equal left- and right-handed forms) that is detrimental to life—proteins in living things contain only left-handed amino acids (with few exceptions). No natural process is known that makes only left-handed amino acids. The question now is, "Did Miller's experiments really produce the basic building blocks of life?" Since they produced a mixture of a few amino acids, the answer is clearly "No."

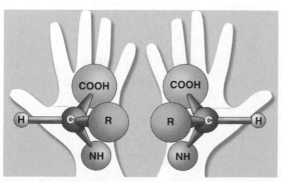

One of the barriers to life forming spontaneously is the occurrence of right- and left-handed molecules. The proteins present in living things contain only left-handed amino acids. Random chemical reactions result in a mixture of both forms—a situation that is toxic to life.

What about information? Every living cell contains a code (A-T, C-G sequence) that originates from a sender (DNA) and is passed to a receiver (RNA) that translates the meaning of the code to produce a protein that is intended to be used by the cell for various functions. If any of the pieces are missing, there is no information, and the cell cannot function properly. Evolutionary hypotheses must be able to explain the origin of this information system and provide a mechanism to increase the amount of information over time. No known natural law can provide a mechanism to accomplish this task. DNA is an amazingly efficient storage device. A one-square-inch chip of DNA could store the information in over 7 billion Bibles—millions of times better than current technology. Biblical creationists have no trouble explaining the presence of such complex information—it was created by the most intelligent Being in the universe.

Evolutionists often claim that, given enough time, evolution was certain to happen. Consider that Bradley and Thaxton calculated the formation of a 100-amino-acid protein assembling by random chance to be 4.9×10^{-191}. It is generally accepted that any event with a probability beyond 1×10^{-50} is impossible, so we must conclude that evolution, requiring thousands of times this amount of complexity, is not likely to occur even if the entire universe were full of organic precursors. Naturalism and materialism can offer no realistic method for the origin of life on earth.

5:4 What went wrong at NASA? Faulkner, www.answersingenesis. org/articles/am/v3/n1/what-went-wrong-at-nasa

From the launch of Sputnik in 1957, mankind has been looking to outer space with many different motives in mind. Through the progression of the Mercury, Gemini, and Apollo programs, the U.S. was able to land men on the moon. As interest in the space program waned, the reusable space shuttles were developed to reduce costs, but the shuttle program has not lived up to its expectations. Many worthy, far less expensive, unmanned missions were canceled over the years. The golden years of NASA under the leadership of the creationist Wernher von Braun ended in the 1970s.

Many changes have taken place at NASA including the launching of the Origins program. This program is aimed at searching the universe for the evolutionary beginning of the stars, the earth, and life. Space exploration has shown how special the earth is and has also born out the predictions of biblical creationists.

NASA's search for earth-like planets is aimed at affirming evolution. These scientists believe that identifying planets with water and other characteristics of earth will support their claim that if life could evolve on earth, it must have evolved elsewhere in the universe. Those discovered thus far are quite different from earth. As Christians, we can look at all of these efforts as a way that God will be praised and the uniqueness of the earth will be understood as God has revealed it in His Word.

5:5 The origin of life: a critique of current scientific models, Swee-Eng, www.answersingenesis.org/home/area/magazines/TJ/docs/tjv10n3_origin_life.pdf

This article provides an exhaustive discussion of the topics surrounding the origin of life. The discussion ranges from the presence of oxygen in the early atmosphere (despite the fact that it prohibits the formation of organic molecules) to the formation of DNA molecules and the complexity of the genetic code. Numerous evolutionary papers from scien-

Even if scientists could successfully form life in the laboratory, it would only prove that an intelligent being can create life from matter and energy that already exist. Evolution requires that life arises by itself from matter. Claims that computer programs have demonstrated evolution are false. These programs only show that when you program a computer with a goal, it will eventually accomplish that goal.

"LIFE BY CHANCE" DEMONSTRATION

THE COMPLEXITY OF LIVING THINGS DOES NOT REQUIRE THE WORKINGS OF AN INTELLIGENT DESIGNER. IT IS MERELY THE PRODUCT OF CHANCE AS I'VE SHOWN HERE.

Program designer 100% biased AGAINST God!

Computer programmed to produce a PREDETERMINED result

LIFE=CHANCE

WHAT IS THE CHANCE THAT THERE IS NO CHANCE IN THIS DEMONSTRATION TO BEGIN WITH?!?!!

tific journals are used as evidence to support the idea that life could not have formed on earth by natural causes.

5:6 Could monkeys type the 23rd Psalm? www.answersingenesis. org/home/area/tools/xnv2n3.asp

Let us imagine a special typewriter, "user-friendly" to apes, with 50 keys, comprised of 26 capital letters, 10 numbers, one space bar, and 13 symbols for punctuation, etc. For the sake of simplicity we shall disregard lower-case letters and settle for typing all to be in capitals, and we shall disregard leap years.

How long would it take an operator, on the average, to correctly type Psalm 23, by randomly striking keys? To obtain the answer, let us first consider the first verse of the Psalm, which reads: "THE LORD IS MY SHEPHERD, I SHALL NOT WANT."

According to the Multiplication Rule of the Probability (in simplified form) the chance of correctly typing the three designated letters THE from possibilities is 1 in 50 x 50 x 50, which equals 125,000. At a rate of one strike per second, the average time taken to make 125,000 strikes is 34.72 hours.

Despite many different calculations that demonstrate the virtual impossibility of the formation of even a single piece of DNA, there are those who accept evolution as a fact of nature.

The chance of randomly typing the eight keys (seven letters and one space) in the right sequence of the two words THE LORD is 1 in 50 x 50 eight times (i.e., 508). This is 1 chance in 39,062 billion. There are 31,536,000 seconds in a year, so the average time taken in years to make 39,062 billion strikes at the rate of one strike per second would be 1,238,663.7 years.

The time taken on average to correctly type the whole of verse 1 of Psalm 23, which contains 42 letters, punctuation, and spaces, would be 5042 divided by 31,536,000 (seconds in a year), which is 7.2 x 1063 years.

And the time taken on the average to correctly type the whole of Psalm 23, made up of 603 letters, verse numbers, punctuation, and spaces, would be 50603 divided by 31,536,000 which is 9.552 x 101016 years. If the letter b stands for billion (109), this could be written as about one bbbbbbbbbbbbbbbbbbbbbbbbbbbbbbbbbbbbbbbbbbbbbbbb bbbbbbbbbbbbbbbbbbbbbbbbbbbbbbbbbbbbbbbbbbbbbbbb bbbbbbbbbbbbbbbbbbbbbbb years.

By comparison, the evolutionists' age of the earth is (only) 4.6 billion years, and the evolutionists' age of the universe is (only) almost 15 billion years.

Questions to Consider

1. Since the first cells formed from compounds in the environment, how did the cells develop the information to make those compounds and then assemble them into complex structures?

2. Where did the lipids (fats) come from in the earth's early environment?

3. How accurately can we know what the "primitive" earth's atmosphere was like billions of years ago?

4. Is the origin of life something that science can really help us understand? Are there too many unknown aspects to consider origins a valid scientific field of study?

5. Since scientists accept that the environment used in the Miller experiment never existed, why is it still included in the textbooks as an explanation for how components of life may have formed?

6. Since scientists reject spontaneous generation happening today, why do they accept that it happened in the past?

7. Thomas Huxley argued that the 23rd Psalm could be typed by monkeys if given enough time. He considered this evidence for the possibility of evolution. Who supplied the monkeys with paper, typewriters, and a language system (how did matter originate if it created life)?

8. We know from observational science that everything that comes into existence has a cause. What caused the big bang and the presence of matter in the universe?

9. Why is the idea of panspermia (life coming from another planet) an acceptable scientific hypothesis if creation is not?

10. Isn't the hypothesis of panspermia just as "untestable" as creation?

11. What evidence would be grounds for rejecting the origin of life from nonliving matter? If it is not falsifiable, then why is it considered scientific?

12. If scientists could form life in the laboratory from nonliving matter, wouldn't that only prove that intelligence is required to bring life into existence?

13. Since no one has ever seen life form from nonliving matter, scientists must accept that it happened by faith. Isn't this a religious position?

Tools for Digging Deeper

(see a complete list in the Introduction)

The New Answers Book 1 & 2 by Ham et al.

The Biblical Basis for Modern Science by Henry Morris

The Biotic Message by Walter ReMine

Creation: Facts of Life by Gary Parker

Evolution: A Theory in Crisis by Michael Denton

Evolution: The Fossils Still Say No! by Duane Gish

In Six Days by John Ashton

In the Beginning Was Information by Werner Gitt

The Lie: Evolution by Ken Ham

Not by Chance by Lee Spetner

On the Seventh Day by John Ashton

www.answersingenesis.org/go/origin

www.answersingenesis.org/go/alien

THE ORIGIN OF MICROORGANISMS

In tracking the emergence of the eukaryotic cell one enters a kind of wonderland where scientific pursuit leads almost to fantasy. Cell and molecular biologists must construct cellular worlds in their own imaginations. ... Imagination, to some degree, is essential for grasping the key events in cellular history.

—B.D. Dyer and R.A. Obar, *Tracing the History of Eukaryotic Cells,* Columbia University Press,1994, pp. 2–3

What You Will Learn

According to evolution, once life had spontaneously formed on earth it underwent amazing changes. The exact pattern of these changes is greatly disputed, and molecular evidence is calling the accepted order of bacterial evolution into question. In the evolutionary story, single-celled organisms had to develop ways to cope with an ever-changing environment. As oxygen and radiation levels changed, new information appeared to accommodate these changes in the environment. Multicellular life flourished in the "prehistoric" oceans, and certain organisms began to use others for food. Eventually, photosynthesis allowed an alternative lifestyle, and fungi and plants appeared. The appearance of sexual reproduction offered another benefit that was exploited by certain organisms.

The problem with the above account is that it is all just a story. Virtually no evidence supports the statements, but "they must have happened" or life wouldn't exist in the forms we see today. This circular reasoning lends little support to the theory of evolution. The amazing diversity that appears "suddenly" in the geologic Cambrian Period (known as the Cambrian explosion) is another difficulty for evolutionists to explain. This sudden appearance of complex multicellular organisms is evidence in favor of fully formed complex organisms being created at one point in history. Despite the fact that evolution can accommodate explanations of the usefulness of certain features, it cannot explain—with supporting evidence—how these features came into existence. The evidence confirms the biblical account that God supplied the information for these complex features when He created each kind.

What Your Textbook Says about the Origin of Microorganisms

Evolutionary Concept	Glencoe	PH-Campbell	PH-Miller	Holt	Articles
Prokaryotes are more "primitive" than eukaryotes and occur earlier in the fossil record.	173	114	427	58, 259, T259	6:1
Prokaryotes appear 3.5 billion years ago as fossil stromatolites. Eukaryotes appear later in the fossil record.	377, 456	300, 356	173	57, 258	6:1, 6:2
Multicellular organisms evolved many times over 700 million years ago.	—	—	498	261, 416, 461, 618	6:3
Fungi evolved from eukaryotes 400 million years ago.	458	—	—	482	3:7
Eubacteria and archaebacteria evolved from a common ancestor based on interpretations of molecular evidence.	484	361	472	258, 413–414	5:5, 6:4
Organisms evolved to live in an environment with increasing oxygen due to photosynthesis.	490–491	366	426	—	5:5, 6:5

Evolutionary Concept	Glencoe	PH-Campbell	PH-Miller	Holt	Articles
Protists are generally grouped by characteristics because their evolutionary relationships are very complex and based on DNA evidence.	—	T378, 380–381, 396–397	498	461	3:6, 3:7
Protists evolved from eukaryotes over a billion years ago.	520–521	395–397	498, 506	460	3:7
Fungi, plants, and animals all evolved from protists hundreds of millions of years ago.	543	395	536	261, 460	3:6, 3:7
Fungi evolved with plants in a symbiotic relationship.	—	411	537, T537, 541	—	3:6
Mitochondria and chloroplasts evolved as primitive prokaryotes and were absorbed by other cells—known as the Endosymbiont Hypothesis.	384–385	T128, 395–397	171, 180, T180, 427, T427	65–66, 259–260, T260	6:6
Sexual reproduction first evolved in protists.	318	193	428	461	3:6, 6:7

Note: Page numbers preceded by "T" indicate items from the teacher notes found in the margins of the Teacher's Edition.

What We Really Know about the Origin of Microorganisms

Evolutionists must explain how cells, once they emerged from lifeless matter, diversified into the many life forms we see today. It is supposed that some extinct ancestor of the archaebacteria and eubacteria developed the necessary biologic machinery to survive in diverse situations. There is no evidence for this transformation other than the interpretation of molecular studies extrapolated backwards for billions of years. One major problem for the development of early unicellular organisms is the presence of oxygen in the atmosphere. It is becoming clear that there is no evidence from geology that there was ever a time in earth's history when oxygen wasn't present. The earliest fossil organisms are of oxygen-producing bacteria that form structures known as stromatolites; so any previous organisms must come from imagination, not evidence.

As bacteria continued to evolve on the primitive earth, they supposedly developed many

> As more information is gathered about the molecular structure of different organisms, the way phylogenetic trees are structured is changing. Recent research and papers on the topic of ancestry are making it harder for evolutionists to determine the line of descent. The data—when interpreted in an evolutionary framework—seems to be pointing to a maze of interconnecting lines and not a single tree with distinct branches.

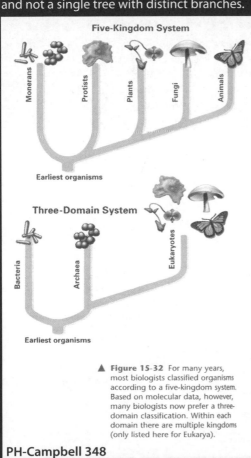

Five-Kingdom System

Monerans · Protists · Plants · Fungi · Animals

Earliest organisms

Three-Domain System

Bacteria · Archaea · Eukaryotes

Earliest organisms

▲ **Figure 15-32** For many years, most biologists classified organisms according to a five-kingdom system. Based on molecular data, however, many biologists now prefer a three-domain classification. Within each domain there are multiple kingdoms (only listed here for Eukarya).

PH-Campbell 348

complex internal structures, what we call organelles today, and supported them inside membranes. The nucleus formed and became enclosed in a membrane with selective proteins that maintain the integrity of the DNA.

Another popular theory is that the mitochondria and chloroplasts are actually endosymbionts—organisms that were "eaten" by a host, but not digested. Somehow, these ingested cells reproduced in harmony with the host, providing some benefit to each. Eventually, DNA was passed from the ingested cell to the nucleus of the host, and the cells became intertwined forever. The fact that there is no real evidence to support this idea is generally ignored. Evidence against the theory is ignored because there is no other accepted naturalistic explanation that accounts for the presence of these organelles.

The process of evolving from a "simple" prokaryote into a "complex" eukaryote is not documented in the fossil record. Despite the lack of evidence, sequences like the one shown in this picture are presented as an explanation in the evolutionary story. It is believed by many evolutionists that the mitochondria and chloroplasts found in eukaryotic cells were actually free-living bacteria that were absorbed but not digested by an ancestral cell line. The endosymbiont hypothesis uses molecular data as support, but the explanation is full of loose language that "may suggest" how the process happened over millions of years.

▼ **Figure 17-18** Eukaryotic cell organelles may have evolved through a combination of two processes. Infolding of the plasma membrane could have produced internal membranes. Certain prokaryotes could have become residents within larger host cells, eventually evolving into mitochondria and chloroplasts.

PH-Campbell 395

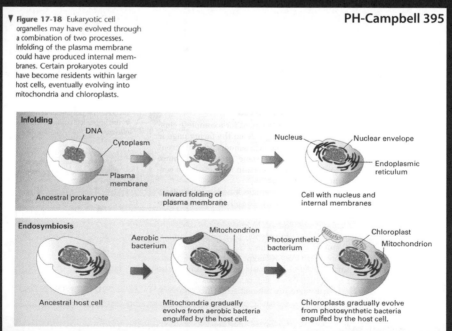

Infolding
DNA
Cytoplasm
Plasma membrane
Ancestral prokaryote
Inward folding of plasma membrane
Nucleus
Nuclear envelope
Endoplasmic reticulum
Cell with nucleus and internal membranes

Endosymbiosis
Aerobic bacterium
Mitochondrion
Ancestral host cell
Mitochondria gradually evolve from aerobic bacteria engulfed by the host cell.
Photosynthetic bacterium
Chloroplast
Mitochondrion
Chloroplasts gradually evolve from photosynthetic bacteria engulfed by the host cell.

As life continued to evolve, multicellular organisms formed as colonies of cells cooperated for mutual benefit. Exactly how a colony of individuals produced a reproductive method that forms the many different cell types needed is not understood and, therefore, is ignored in textbooks. Evolutionists insist that it happened, though—because we are here. Multicellular protists, like algae, were the product of this process of diversification that happened at a time when the earth was supposedly going through many globe-covering ice ages. The evolution of life is a miracle in itself, but the fact that it happened in an environment that alternated between freezer and oven conditions makes it all the more surprising. Evolutionists suggest that the multiple types of eukaryotic life, from protists to mammals, all arose from a common ancestor, but in several distinct lines. The lines that turned into algae and plants contained chlorophyll and mitochondria, and those that turned into animals contained only mitochondria (or may have lost their chlorophyll).

The most striking feature of this part of the evolutionary story is the lack of evidence. Life supposedly started hundreds of millions of years before the first fossils were formed. An understanding of how the three domains of living things (archaebacteria, eubacteria, and eukaryotes) are related has changed significantly. The rapid appearance of multicellular life seen in the Cambrian explosion produces more questions than answers, and the lack of fossil evidence does not support the claims made as to how life advanced into the forms we see today.

Another major event at this point in the evolutionary storyline is the arrival of sexual reproduction. No effective hypothesis can explain the origin of sexual reproduction. In his book *Climbing Mount Improbable*, Richard Dawkins, a leading evolutionary proponent, says:

> To say, as I have, that good genes can benefit from the existence of sex whereas bad genes can benefit from its absence, is not the same thing as explaining why sex is there at all. There are many theories of why sex exists, and none of them is knock-down convincing ... .
> Maybe one day I'll summon up the courage to tackle it in full and write a whole book on the origin of sex.

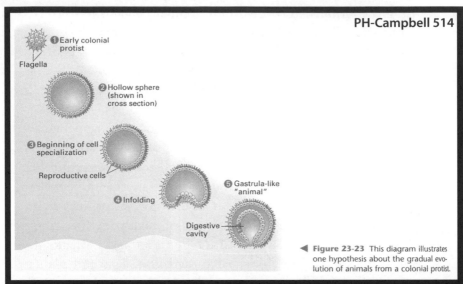

PH-Campbell 514

① Early colonial protist

Flagella

② Hollow sphere (shown in cross section)

③ Beginning of cell specialization

Reproductive cells

④ Infolding

⑤ Gastrula-like "animal"

Digestive cavity

◀ **Figure 23-23** This diagram illustrates one hypothesis about the gradual evolution of animals from a colonial protist.

Though this figure seems to present a scenario for the development of multicellular life, there is no evidence for its accuracy. The textbooks use phrases like "evolutionary milestone" and "appearance of key adaptations" to tell a story that has no basis in science. The textbooks make no attempt to explain how the genetic information developed that could allow a change from individuals to groups of cells exhibiting different developmental pathways and performing different tasks.

The evolution of sexual reproduction is rarely mentioned in textbooks or given more than a just-so statement of the fact that it happened. How two individuals of the same species could have acquired the mutations that would have led to only passing on half of their chromosomes, in a very complex process known as meiosis, and then mated at the exact same time and place in evolutionary history is nothing less than a miracle. The advantages to sexual reproduction are often provided as evidence for evolution, but the mechanism is rarely explained. Just because something would offer an advantage does not mean that it would develop.

Starting with the Bible as a foundation, the interpretation of the existence of single-celled and multicelled organisms is simple. Their apparent similarities point to a divine Creator, not a common ancestor. As we learn more about the complexity of living things and the record that has been left in the rocks, it becomes clearer that life did not evolve from simple to more complex organisms, but that they were created to reproduce "after their kind."

Reference Articles

6:1 Supposed eukaryote evolution pushed back one billion years, Oard, www.answersingenesis.org/tj/v15/i1/eukaryote.asp

Traces of compounds (hydrocarbons called "steranes") produced by eukaryotes (single-celled organisms with membrane-bound organelles) found in 1999 pushed back the arrival of eukaryotes from 1.2 to 2.7 billion years ago. The evolutionary story that had supposed it was difficult for eukaryotes to evolve had to be dramatically reworked. This also presents a challenge to thinking about the early atmosphere because oxygen would have needed to be present to produce the compounds found. This is just another example of the history of life being dramatically changed based on new fossil evidence found and interpreted in the evolutionary framework. Of course, there is no need to change the creation model in light of this evidence. The organisms were all created at the same time and are expected to occur in the oldest sedimentary rocks correlating to the Flood.

6:2 Ancient organisms stay the same, www.answersingenesis.org/creation/v21/i3/news.asp

A while ago, evolutionists would not have expected to find any fossils in rocks that they thought were, say, three billion years old—life supposedly hadn't evolved yet. However, fossils of bacteria kept turning up in progressively older rocks (no surprise to creationists), which allowed less and less time for the first life to evolve in the hypothetical, oxygen-free early atmosphere. Now an Austrian/Swiss team of scientists has looked at rock from Western Australia's Pilbara region, supposedly around 3.5 billion years old, and found fossilized cyanobacteria. These appear to be indistinguishable from the same (oxygen-producing) creatures making the mat structures called stromatolites in the shallows of Shark Bay, some 500 kilometers away on the coast.

6:3 "Snowball Earth"—a problem for the supposed origin of multicellular animals, Oard, www.answersingenesis.org/tj/v16/i1/snowball.asp

Evolutionary scientists suggest that several ice ages that occurred hundreds of millions to billions of years ago actually extended to the equator—the "snowball earth" hypothesis. A major problem is that the snowball condition would be permanent unless there was some catastrophic event to reverse it. Evolutionists face a major problem. Life was supposed to be evolving into multicellular forms at this time—a difficult task in light of a global ice age. Rock formations also suggest a very hot period immediately after, and sometimes during, these ice ages.

To accommodate this, a freeze-fry model was created that allowed the rapid diversification of multicellular life. Volcanoes penetrated the ice and spewed carbon dioxide into the atmosphere, increasing temperatures through the greenhouse effect. A rapid reversal of temperature provided an opportunity for organisms to diversify. Not only did this happen once but five times in the evolutionary model. These cycles limit the likelihood of evolution occurring even further. There are many other significant problems with the model, and computer simulations have failed to show its viability. Trying to explain the explosion of life at the beginning of the Cambrian Period while accommodating climate extremes has proven an impossible puzzle for evolutionists to solve. Creationists can explain the rock evidence in terms of underwater landslides and rock formation during the hot-ocean phase of the Genesis Flood. The abrupt appearance of multicellular organisms is also easily accounted for in the account of creation.

6:4 Round and round we go—proposed evolutionary relationships among archaea, eubacteria, and eukarya, Purdom, www.answersingenesis.org/cec/docs/evolutionary-relationships.asp

In 1977 Carl Woese first identified what he called a third domain of life, named archaea, based on ribosomal RNA (rRNA) sequence comparisons. The other two domains of life are eubacteria (true bacteria, prokaryotes) and eukarya (protists, fungi, plants, animals, and humans). Archaea share some physical characteristics with eubacteria but tend to live in more extreme environments, such as hot springs and high-salt environments. These extreme environments were believed to be present on early earth; hence archaea were thought to be the ancestor to both eubacteria and eukarya. However, further analyses of archaea showed them to be genetically and biochemically quite different from eubacteria, and they are no longer believed to be ancestral to eubacteria.

Archaea are actually more genetically similar to eukaryotes than eubacteria and are often represented as a "sister" to eukarya on evolutionary trees of life. Eukarya have genes that appear to have come from both archaea and eubacteria, and so a genome fusion has been proposed. Archaea have given eukarya their informational genes (genes for transcription, translation, etc.), and eubacteria have given eukarya their operational genes (genes for amino acid biosynthesis, fat biosynthesis, etc.). Rather than an evolutionary "tree" of life, a "ring" of life has been suggested. The archaea and eubacteria (possibly multiple ones) fused using the processes of endosymbiosis and lateral gene transfer to give rise to eukarya.

A subheading in a recent article discussing the challenges of determining evolutionary relationships among these three groups says it well: "More good theories for eukaryotic origins than good data." The scientists are so locked into their evolutionary assumptions that they must keep reinterpreting the data to fit their theories. If they would interpret their data in light of the truth found in the Bible, they would find that the data fits the creation model much better.

God created many individual kinds of archaea, eubacteria, and eukarya. Through the processes of natural selection and speciation, the many different bacterial, plant, and animal species we have today have developed. The common traits seen among these living organisms point to a common designer not a common ancestor.

6:5 Shining light on the evolution of photosynthesis, Swindell, www.answersingenesis.org/tj/v17/i3/photosynthesis.asp

The evolution of photosynthesis appears to be an impossible process as the intermediate products are toxic to the cell. In the absence of all of the enzymes being present at once, the process would kill the cells it was happening in. The probability of all of the enzymes evolving simultaneously makes it virtually impossible that photosynthesis occurred by chance in "primitive" bacteria. This article describes the process of photosynthesis to expose the evolutionary hurdles that would need to be overcome. The challenges to the evolution of photosynthesis include the presence of 17 enzymes required to assemble chlorophyll and the toxicity of intermediate molecules required to chemically synthesize the enzymes. Natural selection cannot explain the presence of useless enzymes waiting for a functional product, or the presence of other irreducibly complex components.

It defies common sense to imagine that the irreducible complexity of photosynthetic systems would have formed according to evolutionary theory. Rather, the incredible organization and intricacy evident in photosynthesis—a process man has yet to fully understand, let alone copy—screams for a designer. If photosynthesis was present from the beginning, the "oxygen revolution" was never a condition that evolving life had to deal with. Having been created by God, life on earth was already equipped to deal with such issues.

6:6 "Nonevolution" of the appearance of mitochondria and plastids in eukaryotes—challenges to endosymbiotic theory, Purdom, www.answersingenesis.org/cec/docs/endosymbiotic-theory.asp

Endosymbiont theory was first developed and popularized by Lynn Margulis in the early 1980s. The idea proposes that mitochondria were originally protobacteria that were engulfed by an ancestral cell but not digested. As a result, this ancestral cell became heterotrophic (i.e., human and animal cells). Plastids (i.e., chloroplasts) were origi-nally cyanobacteria that were engulfed by an ancestral cell but not digested. This ancestral cell became autotrophic (i.e., plants). These organelles share some characteristics with bacteria including circular DNA, division by binary fission, and membrane and ribosome similarities.

On the surface this process seems simple, but these organelles and their relationship to the cell are extremely complex. For example, not all the proteins necessary for the functioning of the organelles are found in their own genomes. Instead, some of the protein codes are found in the nucleus of the cell. Organelle proteins not made in the organelle must be transferred into the organelle. This involves complex protein transfer machinery comprised of multiple pathways, each involving numerous proteins for the transport of proteins into mitochondria and plastids. How does a transport pathway made of multiple parts, all necessary for the proper functioning of that pathway, evolve in slow incremental steps? It can't because of evolution's "use it or lose it" mechanism; so it must have been designed by a Creator God all at once and fully functional.

6:7 Evolutionary theories on gender and sexual reproduction, Harrub and Thomson, www.trueorigin.org/sex01.asp

One concept that is rarely mentioned in the evolution-ary storytelling is the origin of sexual reproduction (sex). The idea of survival of the fittest seems to fail to explain the origin of sex, even if it may be able to explain why it would be maintained once it had developed. Asexual reproduc-tion is a very effective method of reproduction compared to sex. Several hypotheses have been proposed to explain the origin of sex.

The Lottery Principle suggests that asexual reproduc-tion is like buying many lottery tickets with the same number. Sex allows a mixing of genes; so it is like buying many tickets with many different number combinations.

The Tangled Bank Hypothesis suggests that sex orig-inated to simply prepare the offspring for the variety of challenges they would face in the environment. The intense competition makes sex an advantage.

The Red Queen Hypothesis suggests that sex gives the offspring an advantage in the constant competition to simply maintain its position in the "genetic arms race." Organisms must be constantly undergoing genetic changes just to be able to continue to survive in their environment—they must constantly run just to stay in place. Sex would certainly be an advantage in such a scenario.

The DNA Repair Hypothesis suggests that an advantage is obtained if an organism has two copies of any given gene. The bad copy is less likely to cause problems if there is a chance that the other copy is good. The more genes you have, the less likely you are to suffer from genetic diseases. This would prevent bad genes from affecting a population rapidly and provide a mechanism for the preservation of favorable traits.

Each of these hypotheses, or some combination of them, provides a reasonable explanation for the benefit of sex once it is present, but none address its actual origin. Just because something has a benefit does not mean that it must happen. Neither do these hypotheses address the physical development of male and female sex organs and behaviors. The language used by evolutionists when discussing the particulars of the origin of sex is riddled with phrases like "perhaps some could," "may have been," "by chance," and "over time." All of these are devoid of any evidence. The highly complex nature of sexual reproduction and life on earth clearly points to God as the Intelligent Creator.

Questions to Consider

1. How, exactly, did sexual reproduction originate?

2. Do scientists just accept that sexual reproduction must have evolved because it exists, even though they can't explain how it happened?

3. Sexual reproduction certainly has advantages, but how did the first two sexually reproducing organisms obtain all of the abilities needed at the same time? Males and females would have had to evolve simultaneously while still reproducing to continue the survival of the species.

4. Since multicellular animals evolved at multiple times, wouldn't sexual reproduction have to evolve independently several times? How likely is it that the same process (meiosis) would develop multiple times in the same way?

5. Since all the components of the first cell came from the environment, how did it get the ability (information) to make or assemble these components?

6. Since there is no evidence of life before 3.5 billion years ago, how can we be sure it was there? Is this an example of faith?

7. Since the nuclear membrane is intended to prevent DNA contamination, how did a bacterium get its DNA into the nucleus of another cell and then evolve into a chloroplast or mitochondria?

Tools for Digging Deeper

(see a complete list in the Introduction)

Darwin's Black Box by Michael Behe

In the Beginning Was Information by Werner Gitt

The Biotic Message by Walter ReMine

07

THE ORIGIN OF PLANTS

In virtually all cases a new taxon appears
for the first time in the fossil record with
most definitive features already present,
and practically no known stem-group forms.

–Kemp, T. S. (Curator of Zoological Collections, Oxford
University), *Fossils and Evolution*, Oxford University Press,
1999, p. 246

What You Will Learn

Evolution claims that plants descended from algae as they colonized the empty landmass. Plants couldn't have evolved until there was a sufficient ozone layer to block radiation. The many structures that plants require in order to overcome gravity, keep from drying out, and reproduce would have to have developed gradually over millions of years. Molecular and fossil evidence has complicated the evolutionary model that explains how plants evolved from simple to complex forms. The simple groups are evolutionary dead ends; so plants must have evolved simultaneously in several different ways. Seed plants are alleged to have had an advantage over other ancient plants, and they dominated the landscape. The ancient forests are the source for the different coal beds in evolutionary theory. Flowering plants were the most recent to appear since leaves were remodeled to attract pollinators and accomplish reproductive functions.

Despite this evolutionary story, the Bible describes the creation of different kinds of plants in Genesis 1. The presence of "living fossil" plants like the *Gingko biloba* tree makes it clear that evolution is a plastic theory that can accommodate both rapid change and stability for hundreds of millions of years. The creation of plants in their many diverse forms is apparent in the intricate design of plant systems and the symbiotic relationships that could not have evolved in a gradual process.

What Your Textbook Says about the Origin of Plants

Evolutionary Concept	Glencoe	PH-Campbell	PH-Miller	Holt	Articles
Plants appear as fossils over 400 million years ago.	458, 560	420	551	265, 490, 502	7:1, 7:3
Plants evolved from green algae and invaded the vacant land niche.	559, 666	420, T420	430, 511, T512, T514, 553, 554, 555	265, 422, 502	7:2, 7:3, 7:4
Many adaptations were needed as plants moved from water onto land.	562, 564, 580	418, T418, 420–425	430, T549, 554, 555, 643, 644, T645	502–505	7:4
Many symbiotic relationships evolved to support plants on land.	—	411	437–438, T438, 542, T553, 615	T266, 362	3:14
Early forests were dominated by giant ferns and cycads that formed fossil fuels. These were later replaced by seed plants.	566, 567, 584	427	T77, 144, 430, 431, 561, 566, 567	266	7:3
The first fossils of vascular plants occur at 375 million years ago.	586–587	427	554, 560, T560, 562, 566	510	7:3
The first fossil seed plants occur at 360 million years ago, as seed plants replace ferns and cycads.	596–597	431-433	564, 566, 568, T571	504	7:3

Evolutionary Concept	Glencoe	PH-Campbell	PH-Miller	Holt	Articles
Flowering plants evolve slowly and appear in the fossils 130 million years ago.	569, 656	434, 436–437, T443, 445, 448, 470, 481–485	432, T432, 569, T612, 618	505, 514	7:3
Bristlecone pines in the Rocky Mountains are the oldest known organisms at 4,700 years old.	—	T454	T567	513, T570	7:5

Note: Page numbers preceded by "T" indicate items from the teacher notes found in the margins of the Teacher's Edition.

What We Really Know about the Origin of Plants

In the evolutionary story, plants arrived relatively late in earth history. The first fossils of plants are supposed to be 475 million years old. Evolutionists generally agree that plants evolved from algae that slowly began to colonize the land. This could not have occurred until after there was an intact ozone layer to protect the plants from some of the atmosphere's harmful UV rays. Since this was an alien land, plants had to adapt to the new landscape. Several key systems had to be developed to prevent drying out (desiccation) in the air, to absorb nutrients from the soil, to grow upright without the support of water, and to reproduce on land.

All of these new features required new information to code for their production. As stated previously, no mechanism can consistently provide new information from random mutations in the genomes of individuals. While plants do have many adaptations that allow them to be successful on land, these features could not have developed through evolution. The many features that allow plants to thrive in diverse environments were programmed into the different plant kinds when they were created by God. This view of adaptation is a key difference in the evolution and creation models. Setting aside evolutionary bias and focusing on operational science, we can define adaptation as:

Adaptation: a physical trait or behavior due to inherited characteristics that gives an organism the ability to survive in a given environment.

In evolutionary biology, adaptations are often acquired by modifying existing structures to accomplish new tasks. In the case of algae turning into plants, the preexisting structures are mostly absent. Few algae have differentiated tissues that could be adapted to a new use. To get around this, some suggest that fungi invaded the land with the plants to help in absorbing nutrients from the soil. There is much evidence of plants and fungi living in symbiotic relationships today, but nothing to suggest that they evolved to help one another.

The first plants to evolve were the small mosses and liverworts (bryophytes), but these evolutionary dead ends did not lead to the vas-

The adaptations shown in this figure allegedly developed over millions of years as plants had to acquire new features to be able to survive on land. Superficially, similarities between the algae and plant are shown, but the information required to produce the new structures and their functions cannot be explained within the evolutionary framework. Each of these groups was created with the features and information they need to survive in the conditions in which they live.

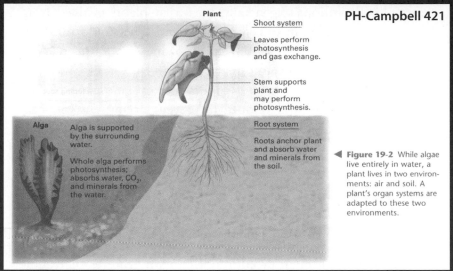

Plant

PH-Campbell 421

Shoot system

Leaves perform photosynthesis and gas exchange.

Stem supports plant and may perform photosynthesis.

Root system

Roots anchor plant and absorb water and minerals from the soil.

Alga

Alga is supported by the surrounding water.

Whole alga performs photosynthesis; absorbs water, CO₂, and minerals from the water.

◄ **Figure 19-2** While algae live entirely in water, a plant lives in two environments: air and soil. A plant's organ systems are adapted to these two environments.

cular plants that are common today. The three groups of bryophytes are found in an unexpected sequence in the fossil record, so evolutionists must accept that they evolved separately from one another. The most likely ancestor is a mobile alga known as a "chlorophyte."

The vascular plants are supposed to have evolved separately from other algae. The ferns, club mosses, and horsetails (pteridophytes) are the suggested common ancestors to the vascular plants that are present in large quantities today. The Carboniferous era is described as having giant ferns and club moss trees, none of which survives today. The vast forests of the Carboniferous are the source of many coal and oil reserves in the evolutionary model.

The next step in the evolutionary story is the development of seed plants. The first to evolve were the gymnosperms, cone-bearing plants like conifers, ginkgo, and cycads. These plants had an adaptive advantage over the pteridophytes and dominated the forests of the late Paleozoic era.

The evolution of flowers and seed protected in a fruit led to the next branch, the angiosperms. The production of flowers and fruits has a cost, but this cost is outweighed by the benefits. And many adaptations have led to diverse types of flowering plants. Along with these new information-gaining changes, many intricate symbiotic relationships supposedly developed. Many exclusive symbiotic relationships exist between fungi, bacteria, and insects. If these relationships are disturbed, the plants either do not survive or are less able to compete. The scenario that explains how a complex symbiotic relationship evolves seems to be a Catch-22 in evolutionary scenarios. If the bee doesn't have a certain shape, it can't get to the nectar, but it is the only bee with the right body shape to distribute the pollen for the flower. If either is not in place, the other does not survive, or it is not as fit as its competitors.

Another problem facing the evolutionary story is the presence of fossil plants that have not changed in hundreds of millions of years. The species *Ginkgo biloba* is known from fossils that are supposed to be 200 million years old. Another "living fossil," the Wollemi pine, was recently discovered in Australia. The oldest fossils of this plant date to over 90 million years. The plastic theory of evolution must accept that these plants are evidence that evolutionary forces can act by holding

The presence of living trees that are virtually identical to fossil species, like the ginkgo shown here and the Wollemi pine, demonstrates the failure of evolution to make useful predictions. Living and extinct trees are proof that evolution can keep things the same for hundreds of millions of years or make drastic changes—take your pick.

still for millions of years, even though evolution can explain the rapid appearance of new species. If evolution means that things can evolve fast and slow, how can it be used to make predictions?

Despite the evolutionary story provided for the evolution of plants from algae, the appearance of new information, the symbiotic relationships required, and the sequence of fossils point to a Creator. There is no reconciliation between the two models— plants were created by the Creator, not by chance and time.

Reference Articles

7:1 Precambrian pollen: a response to questions about creationist research, Williams, Chaffin, Howe, et al., www.rae.org/pollen. html

A paper published in 1966 by C. L. Burdick put forth the claim that pollen and other organic material was found in the Hakatai shale of Grand Canyon. If true, this would push back the date of the origin of plants to the Precambrian era. No secular or evolutionary scientists would even bother spending time and money researching such a topic. It has been suggested by various sources that the samples were simply contaminated by modern pollen or that pollen grains had worked their way into cracks in the rocks. Several authors have defended the work and refute the claims of those who challenge the findings. Later papers noted that microspores have also been found in Cambrian rocks in India, Australia, and Russia.

7:2 Did plants evolve? Williams, www.answersingenesis.org/creation/v19/i4/plants.asp

The evolutionary sequence of plants is not displayed in the fossil record even though the story is told in textbooks. At least four different evolutionary lines are supposed to have emerged from prehistoric green algae—the common ancestor of all plants. In a recent text on plants, not a single fossil series is provided to support the phylogenetic trees that explain the evolutionary history of plants. The grand claims are laced with words like "probably," "apparently," and "presumably." The places where the fossil record is the most complete should provide the clearest picture of evolution, but this is where many evolutionists disagree. The lack of fossil ancestors for the major groups would seem to be important, but the evolutionists fill in the gaps with imagination, not science. The evidence clearly points to diverse groups created in the supernatural events described in Genesis.

7:3 Kingdom of the plants: defying evolution, Williams, www.answersingenesis.org/creation/v24/i1/plants.asp

The evolution of plants offers unique challenges to evolutionary scientists. The simplest of plants are said to have evolved at different times from some type of chlorophyte algae, but they did not give rise to the more complex vascular plants. As you move up the evolutionary ladder, there are no known ancestors for a majority of the major phyla of plants, and the chemical relationships do not support the common evolutionary models. Major changes to the organization of the phylogenetic tree of plant evolution have been suggested, but the order of events is still being debated. In many cases, the claimed ancestors appear later in the fossil record.

The major groups of plants appear suddenly and fully formed—the transitional species are not present in the fossil record. To explain the amazing complexity of the "most evolved" plants, those with flowers (angiosperms), evolutionary forces have modified leaves into petals, sepals, anthers, ovaries, and other flower structures over vast ages. This claim is made even though there is no fossil evidence for the changes that occurred and flowering plants appear fully developed in the fossil record. All of this evidence points back to the creation model and the fact that plants are observed, in the present and the fossils, reproducing within preprogrammed limits and "after their kind."

7:4 Islands' weeds don't support evolution, www.answersingenesis.org/creation/v18/i3/weeds.asp

There are many claims of evolution in action, but can these claims really explain the information-adding changes that would be necessary to turn algae into plants? In a study of weeds on an island, it was documented that the type of seeds produced changed over time. Plants that produce seeds that are able to be carried further by the wind were less likely to survive. Over a short period of time, only seeds that travel a short distance were produced by the plants on the islands. Rather than demonstrating how plants could gain new features, this example of natural selection confirms the creationist principle of the conservation of kinds.

7:5 Living tree "8,000 years older than Christ"? www.answersin-genesis.org/creation/v17/i3/living_tree.asp

A group of Huon pines in Tasmania has been claimed as the oldest living organism. Scientists have "dated" the tree at "more than 10,500 years old." From the creationist perspective, it is not possible that any trees much older than 4,500 years could exist since the catastrophic nature of the Flood would most likely have removed all vegetation from the surface of the earth. The age of the group of trees, which are clones based on DNA samples, was not determined by ring counts, but by the presence of pollen in samples drilled from a nearby lake. Traditional tree-ring dates give ages of no more than 4,000 years. This is close to the oldest bristlecone pines from the Rocky Mountains, which have 4,600 rings. The fact that the ages for the Huon pines are estimated from pollen in a nearby lake means the dates are based on many assumptions. One scientist associated with the study noted that the media had run the story prematurely and that the claim was not yet substantiated. Tree

The fact that the age of the oldest known trees corresponds to the biblical date of Noah's Flood cannot be easily explained by evolution. There is no reason that trees much older than 4,500 years should not be found on earth—unless a global catastrophe wiped them out.

dating involves many assumptions, but the fact that the oldest known dates are near 4,500 years confirms the date of the global Flood described in Genesis. Apart from the Flood, there is no reason why trees older than 4,500 years should not be alive today.

Questions to Consider

1. Since there are no known transitional fossils for major plant groups, how can scientists accurately describe their evolution?

2. How do scientists explain the fact that no individual trees are found to be older than about 4,500 years?

3. Do symbiotic relationships represent a kind of Catch-22 for evolution?

4. Since grass is not supposed to have evolved until after the dinosaurs became extinct, why is grass found in dinosaur dung?

5. Why has pollen been found in rocks classified as Precambrian (long before even the earliest plants are supposed to have been present on the earth)?

6. Sexual reproduction would have had to evolve independently in plants and in several different ways. How likely is it that the process of meiosis would evolve many different times in plants, as well as in animals?

Tools for Digging Deeper

(see a complete list in the Introduction)

Evolution: The Fossils Still Say No! by Duane Gish

Not by Chance by Lee Spetner

THE ORIGIN OF INVERTEBRATES

Soft parts, such as skin impressions of dinosaurs, and soft-bodied animals like jellyfish are sometimes preserved, and in some localities may be common, but they give us only brief glimpses of evolutionary histories. Obviously we have no record of the origin of life, and little or no evolutionary history of the soft-bodied organisms. It is hardly surprising, then, that we have so many gaps in the evolutionary history of life, gaps in such key areas as the origin of the multicellular organisms, the origin of vertebrates, not to mention the origins of most invertebrate groups. The creationists, of course, just love to draw attention to these gaps, which they score as points against evolution. We saw ... though, that their case is without foundation, because they have ignored vital evidence from the living world.

–McGowan, C., *In the Beginning ... A Scientist Shows Why the Creationists Are Wrong*, Prometheus Books, 1984, p. 95

What You Will Learn

The appearance of multicellular animals occurs in an event known as the Cambrian explosion. There are few ancestors to these animals in the underlying layers. The appearance and diversity of these invertebrates cannot be explained on the basis of mutations accumulating and being selected for over time. The origin of multicellular life from a group of colonial organisms is a stretch of the imagination and is not based on any physical evidence. The evolutionary relationships are based on assumptions about how the embryos develop and the similarity in their molecular structure. The many complex structures, such as gills, lungs, digestive systems, muscles, and flight structures, that had to evolve did so without a known mechanism.

According to evolutionists, as these organisms continued to evolve, they invaded the land and had to overcome the many challenges that they faced there. Competition for resources, both in the sea and on land, caused a wide variety of body plans to develop. These "evolutionary milestones" occurred at unknown dates and rates, but they must have happened in order for evolution to be true. The presence of many invertebrates that are "living fossils" casts doubt on the way that evolution has occurred. Do hundreds of millions of years lead to change or stability? From the creationist perspective, the sudden appearance of complex life and the presence of "living fossils" are totally consistent with biblical creation. The special creation of diverse organisms and the degree of change within the created kinds over several thousand years is consistent with the evidence seen in the fossil record.

What Your Textbook Says about the Origin of Invertebrates

Evolutionary Concept	Glencoe	PH-Campbell	PH-Miller	Holt	Articles
All animals share a common ancestor that evolved in the primitive seas over 600 (or 700) million years ago from colonial protists.	459, 674	514	429, 660	T592, 594, T594	5:6, 8:1
Many adaptations represent key stages in evolutionary history: nervous system, segmentation, body cavities, bilateral symmetry, etc.	684	T492	658–659, 663, 748–749, 751–752, 756	599, 600, 603, T602, T606, 607, 618, 622, 629, 633, 642, 651, 664, 693, 700	3:6
Evolutionary relationships of animal phyla are based on DNA and molecular evidence due to the lack of fossil evidence of ancestral species.		516–517	429	T601, 602	3:6, 3:7
Studying the embryonic development of invertebrates reveals their evolutionary history.	677	511, 513	T660, 661, 745	692–693, T694, T696	3:7

Evolutionary Concept	Glencoe	PH-Campbell	PH-Miller	Holt	Articles
A wide variety of body plans appears "suddenly" in the fossil record about 550 million years ago—known as the Cambrian explosion.	377, 685	336, 514–515, T515	429, 430, T744, 745, 747	262, T262	4:16
Sponges and cnidarians were the first groups of animals to evolve over 650 million years ago.	681, 705	498, 515	664	619	8:1
Roundworms and flatworms evolved from different ancestors.	707, 733	—	T686, 684	602	8:2
Segmented worms and mollusks evolved in the ocean approximately 550 million years ago. They are closely related based on embryology. The development of excretory systems and eyes occur first in these groups.	724, 729, 733	—	694, 701–703, 704, 706	642, 644, T648, 651, 664	3:7
Lungs and other organs have evolved independently in terrestrial animals, including mollusks and arthropods, as some mollusks lost their shells in recent evolutionary development.	725, 727, 744	—	716	605, 645–646, 649, 668	3:28

Evolutionary Concept	Glencoe	PH-Campbell	PH-Miller	Holt	Articles
Arthropods evolved from annelids over 600 million years ago in three distinct groups. Key adaptations include jointed appendages and an exoskeleton. Exoskeletons allowed arthropods to invade the land about 430 million years ago.	742, 754–755, 785	525, 527	430, T430, T654–655, 715–716, T724	262, 266, 603, 664–665, 674	3:13
Horseshoe crabs have remained unchanged for 300 million years based on fossil evidence.	751	526	439, 723	—	3:19, 4:9
Echinoderms evolved over 650 million years ago. Based on deuterostome development pattern, echinoderms share a recent common ancestor with vertebrates.	765, 769	513	734, 738, T749	693, 697	3:7, 3:13
Flight evolved at least four different times, beginning with arthropods 100 million years before pterosaurs.	—	—	726, 728	595, 678	8:3

Note: Page numbers preceded by "T" indicate items from the teacher notes found in the margins of the Teacher's Edition.

What We Really Know about the Origin of Invertebrates

Invertebrates are certainly the most abundant animals on earth, but how did they get here and how did all of their diverse forms come about? In one of the more popular hypotheses in the evolutionary story, the single-celled organisms (discussed earlier) supposedly began to form colonies. Colonies offer these organisms an unknown advantage; so natural selection leads to more and more colonies. As time passes, these colonial organisms start to develop specialized cells and then form into a ball with an indentation that can ingest things and take advantage of a new food source. Exploiting this new food source leads to more advances, and eventually there are thousands of different invertebrate life forms swimming in the ancient seas. One problem—there is no fossil evidence for the story. The story is based on the comparison of DNA sequences (which relies on many assumptions as discussed earlier) between organisms and a presumed common ancestor.

Within the evolutionary sequence of events, the mechanisms that made the changes are not known, and they cannot be known. Again, the lack of testability and repeatability demonstrates how this subject lies in the realm of historical science, if it is science at all. In order for the colonial protists, or even unicellular protists, to become truly multicellular organisms, an amazing change must happen extremely rapidly. Unicellular organisms cannot produce more than one type of cell. In order to become a multicellular organism, new information must be available that tells the cells to develop in new ways to perform different functions. The source of this new information cannot come

> The simplest animals, sponges, are supposed to have evolved from ancient choanoflagellate protists based on the fact that the larval stage of sponges looks similar to other choanoflagellates that exist today. This could be explained as convergent evolution, but it is used as proof of common descent in this case.

Holt 619

Figure 3 Choanoflagellate. Ancient choanoflagellates similar to the one shown above may be the ancestors of sponges.

from random mutations (as discussed in Chapter 3), but even if it could, a multitude of new functions must be simultaneously added to the genome. The hormonal control of development and cell coordination must be present with the information to code for the hormones and new cell structures. It is insufficient to say that old hormones and proteins get used in a new way because those old hormones and proteins must still perform their original functions or the cell is not as fit and would be removed by natural selection.

Considering this transformation, one cell from the colony has to "know" how to do all of the jobs that the other cells were doing and gain that information from those cells. After it has gained the information, it must then direct the different cell types and orchestrate when the genes are turned off and on within each cell, activities that are not required in unicellular life. The lack of any evidence for this type of evolution makes the scenario that much more unlikely.

At least 95% of known fossils are of invertebrates, but the picture of invertebrate evolution is still very fuzzy. The major reason for this is the sudden appearance of fully formed invertebrate body plans in the fossil layer that records what is known as the Cambrian explosion. The ancestors to the variety of multicellular invertebrates

This illustration shows a representation of some of the forms that appeared very suddenly in the fossil record during the period known as the Cambrian explosion. In the creationist model, these animals represent descendants of original created kinds that became extinct during the Flood of Genesis. Gradual evolution cannot account for the sudden appearance of so many types of life.

PH-Campbell 515

▶ Figure 23-24 An artist created this painting based on data from fossils found in British Columbia, Canada. The scene illustrates some of the diversity of animals that existed during the early Cambrian period.

are not known from fossils. Some traces of multicellular life are found in Precambrian rocks but not the types or abundant variety that would be expected from the diverse organisms in the Cambrian rocks. The cladograms and phylogenetic trees shown in the textbooks differ in their major branching points, and the changing nature of DNA and molecular evidence means that by the time a text is published, the ideas about ancestry may have changed. These models of evolutionary history are just speculative interpretations, and different groups within the scientific community come to different conclusions when they weigh the evidence with different assumptions and biases.

As you read through the evolutionary story in textbooks, you are expected to accept as fact a multitude of just-so statements even though those stories include details that cannot be known. You will see phrases that assume that certain things must have occurred in order for them to exist as they do today. For instance, evolutionists "know" cells must have formed in the ancient oceans because we have cells today. The major advances in invertebrate body plans are treated in this way. The development of soft-tissue features, like nervous systems and body cavities, is rarely preserved in fossil specimens. A statement like, "The development of bilateral symmetry was an important evolutionary adaptation that allowed animals to respond to their environment and compete better for resources" sounds logical, but it is not based on evidence. This statement is not true in itself, but it is a corollary to the evolutionary story. These are often referred to as evolutionary "milestones" or "key adaptations" because they needed to happen for a new kind of organism to form. When you read a statement like this or any statement that expects you to accept something as fact, remember that these are interpretations based on evolutionary assumptions. It is also important to remember that these ideas have probably changed in the recent past and will change in the near future as naturalistic scientists reinterpret the evidence with ever-changing ideas. While change is expected in science as new knowledge is gained, the fact that new data is constantly interpreted in the failed framework of evolution, regardless of how well it fits, demonstrates the importance of presuppositions and the prior commitment to a naturalistic explanation.

As invertebrates diversified in "prehistoric" oceans, evolutionists suggest that their nervous systems became more complex and that structures that sense the environment (light, vibration, chemical detection, etc.) gave these new animals an advantage. External skeletons developed in the ocean and allowed animals the opportunity to invade the land where the plants that had already evolved to survive on land could provide many open niches and food sources.

Another interesting observation comes when you analyze the dates given in different textbooks. Many of the evolutionary "milestones" and "first" fossils are given extremely different dates in different textbooks. This is true in most cases, from bacteria to the "most recent" divergent paths in evolution. The age of the first animal fossils differs by 100 million years between textbooks, and many other dates differ by varying degrees depending on which authority you use. The variation in dates given by different experts exposes the speculative nature of evolutionary storytelling, regardless of the supposedly objective nature of science.

Note: Many of the topics in this section are not dealt with specifically in articles, but the references refer to general arguments that can be applied to specific cases. No articles discuss the details of mollusk evolution, for example, but the arguments for common ancestry, homology, and fossil evidence can be applied to this specific example, as well as other specific cases.

Reference Articles

8:1 AiG answers new TV series on animal evolution, www. answersingenesis.org/docs2002/0404pbs.asp

The PBS series *The Shape of Life* claims that the presence of a common stretch of DNA in all animals points to sponges as the ancestor of all animals. Since fossil sponges from China remarkably resemble living sponges, how can these ancestral sponges remain unchanged for hundreds of millions of years? The fact that animals share common DNA sequences is just as much evidence for a common designer as it is for common ancestry.

8:2 Wormholes in evolutionary scenario, www.answersingenesis.org/creation/v21/i1/news.asp

According to classic evolutionary belief, no animals other than single-celled creatures are supposed to be present in rocks which are dated at more than 580 million years. What appear to be unmistakable worm burrows have now been found in rocks which date around 1.1 billion years. The consistent diameter of the markings helps to identify them as worm burrows and puts worm fossils several hundred million years before animals were supposed to have evolved from colonial protists.

Worms have always been worms; they were made on Day 6 of Creation Week.

8:3 Tail-gliding bugs are not evidence for flight evolution, Tomkins, www.icr.org/article/tail-gliding-bugs-are-not-evidence

Researchers recently suggested, based on experiments that involved dropping bristletails from trees, that flight may have evolved in insects to control aerial descent. Flight

The evolution of echinoderms is believed to be distinct from other invertebrates because of their deuterostome development pattern. Because vertebrates share this feature, echinoderms share an alleged common ancestor with vertebrates.

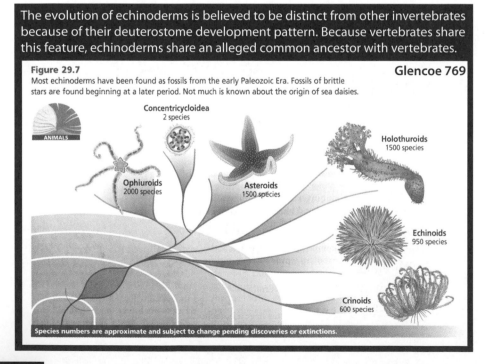

Figure 29.7

Most echinoderms have been found as fossils from the early Paleozoic Era. Fossils of brittle stars are found beginning at a later period. Not much is known about the origin of sea daisies.

Glencoe 769

ANIMALS

Concentricycloidea
2 species

Holothuroids
1500 species

Ophiuroids
2000 species

Asteroids
1500 species

Echinoids
950 species

Crinoids
600 species

Species numbers are approximate and subject to change pending discoveries or extinctions.

is supposed to have evolved at least five times in different animal groups. The problem is that these flyers appear fully formed in the fossil record—we find no partially-formed wings in the fossil record.

These changes would have required hundreds of mutations and an entire framework of nerves, muscles, and connections would have evolve to accompany the wings. Natural selection would actually lead to the removal of partially-developed features that would hinder survival in the wild. This leaves no evidence for flight evolution nor any credible naturalistic story of flight's origin. The wide variety of flying creatures is evidence that confirms the biblical account of the creation of flying things (Genesis 1:21).

Questions to Consider

1. How exactly did colonial organisms get the information required to code for all of the proteins and hormones needed to form different types of cells?

2. How did colonial organisms share genetic information so that a single cell could develop into many cells that perform different functions? Has this ever been replicated in the lab?

3. Does the ability of some new trait ("evolutionary milestones") to give an advantage, like bilateral symmetry, make it likely to evolve? Does evolution offer predictable claims about what advantages are expected to enhance survival? If we don't know what to look for in evolutionary change, how do we know when it has occurred?

4. The dates for the "first" organism of many types of invertebrates seem to be getting older and older as new fossils are found. What will happen to evolutionary theory if there is basically no time between the ancestor and the descendant?

5. It seems that whenever evidence challenges current evolutionary theory, the theory just changes to accept the new data, but the presuppositions don't change. What evidence would scientists accept that would cast doubt on evolution itself?

Tools for Digging Deeper

(see a complete list in the Introduction)

The Biotic Message by Walter ReMine

Creation: Facts of Life by Gary Parker

Darwin's Black Box by Michael Behe

Evolution: The Fossils Still Say No! by Duane Gish

In the Beginning Was Information by Werner Gitt

Not by Chance by Lee Spetner

THE ORIGIN OF VERTEBRATES

The absence of fossil evidence for intermediary stages between major transitions in organic design, indeed our inability, even in our imagination, to construct functional intermediates in many cases, has been a persistent and nagging problem for gradualistic accounts of evolution.

—Gould, S. J., in *Evolution Now: A Century After Darwin*, ed. John Maynard Smith, Macmillan, New York, p. 140, 1982

What You Will Learn

The evolution of organisms with complex internal skeletons is supposed to have occurred around 500 million years ago. Despite the lack of fossil evidence for this supposed transformation, evolutionary beliefs make the acceptance of this prehistoric phase necessary. In spite of the fact that no one knows what the first vertebrate looked like, it is considered the ancestor of all fish, amphibians, reptiles, and mammals that have ever lived. This ancestor would sit at a major branch of the evolutionary tree of life. If this ancestor is not real, the branch that has led to much of the life on earth falls off the tree.

According to evolutionists, after the first fishes had evolved, they dominated the seas and gradually grew legs—another transition that is missing from the fossils. Complex lung structures had to develop, and new reproductive methods had to be in place for the arrival of reptiles. Some unknown ancient reptile gave rise to what we know today as reptiles, birds, and mammals. The countless number of changes in genetic information that would be necessary to make even the smallest of these changes is impossible based on what we know about genetics today. Despite terms like "evolutionary milestone" and "key adaptations" used in the textbook stories of evolutionary history, there is no evidence that these changes actually happened. As we look at the fossil record, fish have always been fish, and mammals have always been mammals. There is certainly a great amount of diversity within all vertebrate groups, but this diversity was preprogrammed into the created kinds by God.

What Your Textbook Says about the Origin of Vertebrates

Evolutionary Concept	Glencoe	PH-Campbell	PH-Miller	Holt	Articles
The first vertebrates were fish that appear in the fossil record 530 million years ago. This group evolved into lampreys, sharks, and bony fishes, eventually becoming amphibians. The origin of these groups is unclear.	775, 792, 800–802	T540, 543–546	430, T766, 772, T772, 840, T848, 849, 850–851, T850, T852, T860–T862	267, 702, T710–T712, 714–717, T714, 751	9:1
The presence of pharyngeal pouches, a post-anal tail, and a backbone in all vertebrate embryos shows they have a common ancestor.	772	302–303, 542	767, 768, T768, 769	286, 700	3:31
The development of a skeleton, gills, a swim bladder, and jaws were key adaptations that allowed vertebrates to diversify in the oceans.	797–798, 818	543, 545, 549	771–773, T772, 774, 777, 860–861	267, 700, 712, 715, T744–T745, 747–749	3:6, 9:2
Amphibians evolved from an unknown fish ancestor 370 million years ago. Developing legs, lungs, and a 3-chambered heart gave them an evolutionary advantage.	807–809	545, T549, 550, 552–553, T553, 555, 558	430, 773, 780, 782–783	14, 267, 718–720, T718, T744, 757–760	9:2, 9:3

Evolutionary Concept	Glencoe	PH-Campbell	PH-Miller	Holt	Articles
Reptiles evolved from amphibians over 340 million years ago. Evolutionary adaptations included lungs, scaly skin, and amniotic eggs. This line eventually evolved into mammals and birds.	817–819, 824–825, 882–883, 1006	558, 560– 562, T560, T796, T798	430, 431, 798–799, 800, 802–803	268, 721, 722, 772, 774–775, 777	9:4
Turtles and tuataras are among the living fossils that have changed little over hundreds of millions of years.	824	563	T804	727, 782–783	4:9, 9:4, 9:5
Dinosaurs dominated the earth 250–85 million years ago. Some dinosaurs may have been warm-blooded based on bone structure. Many key adaptations arose as dinosaurs evolved.	—	562	74, 432, T432, 798–799, 821, 856, T856	722–724	9:6
Mammals were small and nocturnal during the age of the dinosaurs.	—	—	433, T433, 435–436, 821, T825	T724	9:7
Snakes evolved from lizards that lost their legs. Some constrictors still have a vestigial pelvis.	823	563–564	803	779	9:8

Evolutionary Concept	Glencoe	PH-Campbell	PH-Miller	Holt	Articles
Birds evolved from feathered theropod dinosaurs and are closely related to crocodiles. *Archaeopteryx* and other "feathered fossils" demonstrate this relationship.	826, 832–833	290, 346–347	432, 799, 806–807, T807	268, T723, 725–727, 784	2:5, 3:35, 4:17
Feathers are modified protein scales that may have evolved for insulation and were later adapted to flight.	826	566, T568	—	784	2:5, 3:35, 9:9
Birds have adapted to a life of flight by evolving modified forelimbs, feathers, a 4-chambered heart, air sacs, and hollow bones. Some birds have lost their wings through evolution.	827	566	808–809, 851	T725–T726, 726, 784, 790	2:5, 3:35
The first small mammals evolved over 220 million years ago from a therapsid ancestor.	397, 840, 850–851	570–571	431, 802, T820, 822–823	268, 719, 728, T810	9:7
Feathers and hair evolved from reptilian scales. All three contain keratin.*	841	560–561	—	—	9:9
Evolutionary origin of hair is unknown, but it probably did not evolve from reptilian scales.*	—	—	821	800	9:9

Evolutionary Concept	Glencoe	PH-Campbell	PH-Miller	Holt	Articles
The forelimbs of mammals are adapted to different functions.	—	—	822, 826, T863	807, 812–813	3:6, 3:7
Primates evolved 65–85 million years ago.	379	574	T820	731	9:10
Marsupials evolved in Australia due to geographic isolation.	849	301, 339	15	268, 809	9:11
Monotremes are the most primitive mammals based on reptilian characteristics and molecular evidence.	—	571	—	730, 808	9:12
Placental mammals evolved because of the advantage of internal development.	849	—	864	—	9:7
Courtship and mating characteristics develop through sexual selection even though there is a high cost to the individual.	862	—	—	835–836	6:7, 9:13
The ice age that occurred from 2 million to 10,000 years ago had huge mammals that have since become extinct.	—	—	141, 434, T434	728–729, T780	9:14

Note: Page numbers preceded by "T" indicate items from the teacher notes found in the margins of the Teacher's Edition.

* Contradictory claims were presented in the textbooks reviewed.

What We Really Know about the Origin of Vertebrates

The story of the origin of vertebrates picks up where the evolution of invertebrates left off. The fact that vertebrates and echinoderm invertebrates both follow a deuterostome pattern of embryo development links the two in the evolutionary framework. From some common echinoderm-like ancestor, all vertebrates are supposed to have risen through the ranks of evolution.

It should be pointed out that evolution is not considered an upward process that ultimately leads to some goal. The bacteria of today could actually be considered more evolved than humans, as they have been evolving for a longer time. Evolution can be described as the information-gaining process that has led bacteria to evolve into birds. Evolution is also described in terms of losing new functions after they originally develop. These apparently contrary forms of evolution, gaining and losing information, highlight the plastic nature of the theory as it bends to accommodate any new evidence. The apparent loss and gain of functions make the evolutionary story contain a multitude of "naturalistic miracles"— if such things can exist. The evolution of dinosaurs into birds is no different from the evolution of flightless ostriches from some flying

Vertebrates represent the highest level of complexity of organization in the molecules-to-man evolutionary model. Although pictures similar to this one used to be common in textbooks, they have been replaced by pictures and illustrations showing much smaller degrees of change.

ancestor. Evolution can be interpreted in any way necessary as long as the underlying assumption that evolution has occurred is not challenged.

In a simplified version of vertebrate evolution, hagfish and lampreys evolved from some invertebrate chordate, the bony fish and cartilaginous fish evolved from some unknown ancestor of the lamprey group, amphibians evolved from an ancestor of the bony fish, reptiles evolved from amphibians, and birds and mammals evolved from reptiles. The details of how each of these steps occurred is an example of historical science. Major assumptions and inferences fill in the gaps of the story. These gaps are commonly referred to as "milestones" or "key adaptations" and are mentioned in the textbooks without any supporting evidence. In the evolutionist's belief system, these milestones must have happened because we can see the results today.

One of the most glaring problems with the evolutionary story of vertebrates is the lack of transitional forms. As in other fossil groups, major phyla appear abruptly and fully formed in the fossil record. The origin of amphibians from bony fish was thought to be demonstrated in the lobe-finned coelacanth fish. Observations of the fish in their deep-ocean habitat has shown that they don't use their fins to walk on the bottom—a trait that allegedly led to their becoming amphibians. Lungfish were also thought to be ancestors, but lung development has made this an unlikely ancestral group. The recent

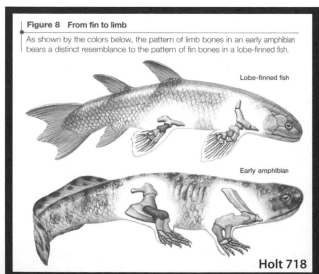

Figure 8   From fin to limb

As shown by the colors below, the pattern of limb bones in an early amphibian bears a distinct resemblance to the pattern of fin bones in a lobe-finned fish.

Lobe-finned fish

Early amphibian

Holt 718

There is no clear agreement on whether the lobe-finned fish are the ancestors to amphibians. The color coding of the bones in this and other pictures is just as much evidence for a common designer as it is for a common ancestor.

Tiktaalik fossils have provided another option, but the lack of appendicular skeletal support structures (shoulders) and the absence of the hind limbs leaves this an unlikely scenario.

After fish had become amphibians, life was primed to invade the land without relying on the water for reproduction. As reptiles evolved, they needed to adapt to a dry environment to exploit an open niche. Scales were needed to prevent the skin from drying out in the open air and provide protection from harmful UV rays. An efficient lung system had to evolve to allow reptiles to move onto land. The evolution of such soft-tissue structures is one area where inferred stories, based on assumptions, are the only source of information. The absence of preserved soft tissue makes interpreting these structures difficult. Reproduction on land requires the development of some mechanism of internal fertilization. Not only did the eggs need to be fertilized internally, they needed to evolve a structure that would protect them from drying out once they were deposited. The development of this amniotic egg requires the genetic information for many new structures. As has been discussed, natural selection cannot create new information needed for molecules-to-man evolution; it can only select for information (traits) that already exist.

Having accomplished the task of evolving into the reptilian form, birds and mammals come next. Both birds and mammals are supposed to have come from different reptilian ancestors. In the most popular bird evolution hypothesis, theropod dinosaurs (the group to which *T. rex* belongs) are represented today by all birds. Birds are professed to be living dinosaurs, a distinction formerly reserved for crocodiles. Exactly how this happened in the course of geologic time is disputed at many levels. The media has placed feathers on dinosaurs when none were found with the fossil remains, and every theropod discovered is described as having feathers. The next time you read a story about a dinosaur find and the description includes details of behavior, coloration, and feather patterns, ask yourself what the evidence is for these inferences that are misleadingly presented as facts. In a vast majority of "feathered dinosaur" fossils there is no evidence of feathers. Recent alleged feathered theropod fossils from China have been exposed as frauds or later reinterpreted as not having feathers. The retraction of the original sensational claims is never as obvious as the fantastic headlines that are stored in the memory banks of the public.

Evolutionary models have a difficult time explaining the development of the many unique characteristics of birds from reptiles. The avian lung has a one-way flow that is interconnected to many small air sacs and a countercurrent blood flow system to maximize the efficiency of gas exchange. How this arose from the billows lung of reptiles is a mystery that evolution cannot accurately explain. Feathers are presented in a contradictory manner in the texts reviewed for this book. The Holt text relates that feathers most likely did not evolve from scales; the Glencoe text states that hair and feathers evolved from scales; and the Prentice Hall text implies the evolution of feathers from scales. This reflects the failure of evolutionary thought to accurately describe a key step in vertebrate evolution.

If evolutionary thought provided the explanatory paradigm that its proponents claim, this issue would not be presented in opposite ways in textbooks. Many other issues within the topic of bird evolution—not to mention evolution in general—are disputed among different groups of scientists. While it is necessary for scientists to question each others' statements and independently verify the results, the speculative nature of the evidence and the

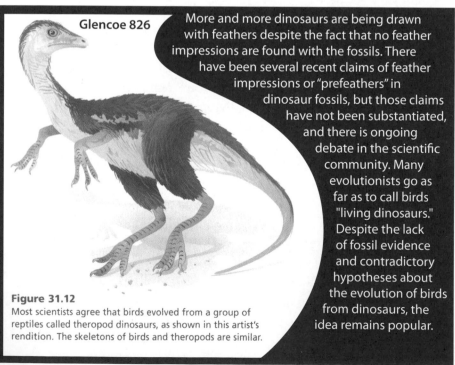

Glencoe 826

More and more dinosaurs are being drawn with feathers despite the fact that no feather impressions are found with the fossils. There have been several recent claims of feather impressions or "prefeathers" in dinosaur fossils, but those claims have not been substantiated, and there is ongoing debate in the scientific community. Many evolutionists go as far as to call birds "living dinosaurs." Despite the lack of fossil evidence and contradictory hypotheses about the evolution of birds from dinosaurs, the idea remains popular.

Figure 31.12
Most scientists agree that birds evolved from a group of reptiles called theropod dinosaurs, as shown in this artist's rendition. The skeletons of birds and theropods are similar.

accompanying explanations leave the debate open to various interpretations. In historical science, like the evolution stories, testing the hypotheses is impossible because they do not represent falsifiable, testable, and repeatable processes. The subjective nature of interpreting supposed evolutionary relationships, whether from cladistics or "molecular clocks," is of questionable validity. Starting with faulty assumptions will lead to faulty conclusions.

In the past, mammals were considered latecomers in evolutionary time. They allegedly hid from the dominant dinosaurs during the day and were only represented by shrew-like creatures that scurried about at night. It was only when the dinosaurs were wiped out that they were able to fill the empty niches. This story has been modified as new discoveries have shown that mammal-like animals (these fossils cannot be evaluated for reproduction and milk production, so they are classified as mammaliaforms) had evolved to live on the land and then invade the water (*Castorocauda lutrasimilis*). This and other discoveries of relatively large mammals have forced evolutionists to rethink the emergence of mammals during the "age of reptiles." Humans are classified as mammals in the evolutionary structure, and the development of hominids will be discussed in the next chapter.

Though evolutionists claim to have a clear, big-picture view of the evolution of vertebrates, the devil is in the details. Just because

Jaws clearly provide an advantage to certain fish in certain situations, but that does not mean that they must have evolved. The simplistic "just-so" jaw evolution story tells us that one piece turned into another without evidence of such a change occurring. The sudden appearance of fully formed jawed fishes and the presence of jawless and jawed fishes today do not support the evolutionary claims.

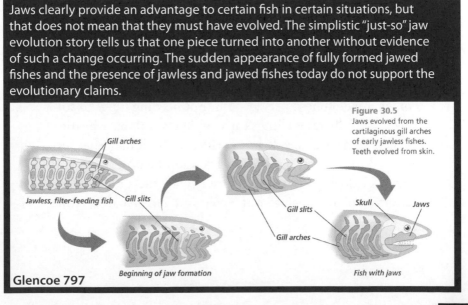

Figure 30.5
Jaws evolved from the cartilaginous gill arches of early jawless fishes. Teeth evolved from skin.

Gill arches

Jawless, filter-feeding fish   Gill slits

Gill slits

Gill arches

Beginning of jaw formation

Skull   Jaws

Fish with jaws

Glencoe 797

things should have happened in a certain way does not mean that they did. The lack of an information-gaining mechanism is still the most effective argument against the growth of the evolutionary "tree of life." The fossil record and living examples of vertebrates support the creationist "orchard" model, with the origin of all vertebrates on Days 5 and 6 of the Creation Week.

Reference Articles

9:1 Oldest vertebrate fossil discovered, dsc.discovery.com/news/afp/20031020/vertebrate.html

> The discovery of a 1.5-inch vertebrate fossil in Precambrian rocks has pushed back the date of the earliest vertebrates by millions of years. This specimen, found in Ediacaran rocks in Australia, looks like a tadpole with clear muscle segments and a vertebrate body plan. Many scientists are skeptical of its features due to the early rocks it is found in, but it is no surprise to creationists. The evolutionary story of the origin of multicellular life is further confounded by this discovery.

9:2 Something fishy about lungs, Vetter, www.answersingenesis.org/creation/v14/i1/lungs.asp

> The presence of swim bladders in many fish would seem to be the logical precursor to lungs as they evolved to inhabit the land. However, the presence of lungs in fossil placoderms and several living fish species shows that lungs may have evolved into swim bladders—the reverse of what would be expected. Fish, not needing lungs to survive, allegedly tested lungs early on in evolutionary history. When lungs were needed to invade the land, the genes just needed to be switched on. The development of lungs and swim bladders is totally consistent with the simultaneous creation of organisms, but evolution has a harder time making it "just so."

9:3 Gone fishin' for a missing link? Menton and Looy, www. answersingenesis.org/go/tiktaalik

The recent discovery of a fossil fish known as Tiktaalik has caused evolutionists to claim that a transitional form between fish and amphibians has been found. The fossil is claimed to be 375 million years old. With its bony forelimbs and its eyes and nostrils atop a flattened head, it is imagined that it lifted itself with its fins while wading through shallow streams. Several problems are apparent when thinking about calling this fossil a transitional form. The bones in the forelimbs are embedded in the muscle and not attached to the axial skeleton, which is the same bone structure in living fish today. The fossils lack the tail and pelvic fins. The presence of bony fins does not mean that the fish is developing into an amphibian. The coelacanth and lungfish that have been claimed as ancestors to modern amphibians in the past have not lived up to the claims, as this new specimen will not. Basing the interpretation on the flawed evolutionary framework will not lead to a true understanding of organisms that "appear" to be evolving.

9:4 Hurdles in the evolution of amphibians to reptiles, Patterson, www.answersingenesis.org/cec/docs/amphibians-reptiles.asp

From an evolutionary viewpoint, amphibians represent a transitional phase as animals began to invade the land. Their characteristics are thought to be intermediate between fish and reptiles. Despite the evolutionary stories about this necessary transformation occurring, the evidence suggests that the hurdles are too great to overcome. The three major characteristics of reptiles that are supposed to have developed through time from an amphibian ancestor are scaly skin, the amniotic egg, and advanced lungs.

The skin of amphibians is arguably more complex than the skin of reptiles. It contains many different glands that are not present in reptile skin, so the transformation to scales involves a loss of information in this regard. Scales develop from folds in the skin; so new information would need to evolve in order to direct the development of this new structure. Amphibians absorb and release gases through their skin as part of their respiration. This thin, permeable skin is alleged to have developed into a thick, waterproof structure—another developmental pathway that would have to appear. As the skin loses the ability to exchange gases, complexity must develop in the lungs of the "emerging" reptiles to accommodate life on the dry land.

Development of an egg that won't dry out on land was another accomplishment that supposedly happened as reptiles evolved. Amphibians must lay their eggs in wet environments to prevent them from drying out. Reptile eggs have a leathery covering that prevents loss of water but still allows gases to be exchanged with the environment. Since there is no record of the molecular and developmental changes that would have had to occur to make this transition, evolution can only provide a colorful story to connect the two through the imaginary expanses of geologic time. Fossil and genetic evidence supports the notion that amphibians have always been amphibians and reptiles have always been reptiles—both groups were created by the Creator to inhabit the earth.

9:5 Turtle scientists shellshocked, www.answersingenesis.org/creation/v18/i4/news.asp

When the rich, diverse, and significant Riversleigh fossil deposits in Northwest Queensland were excavated, scientists found what they described as a new species of "ancient turtle," believed to have gone extinct in the Pleistocene, as long as 50,000 years ago in the evolutionary timescale. About 56 miles downstream from Riversleigh, in Lawn Hill Creek, divers have recently discovered a new turtle species (*Lavarackorum elseya*), which is the same as the fossil Riversleigh one. By having the real thing, Australian scientists saw that they had "wrongly identified" (classified) the fossil turtle, and the living turtle showed no evolutionary change had taken place in all those alleged tens of thousands of years.

"By Faith" by Jim Oliver

Evolutionists believe that humans and dinosaurs never saw one another because the dinosaurs were extinct millions of years before humans evolved. Creationists claim that dinosaurs and humans were present together before and after the Genesis Flood. Dinosaurs would have been present on the Ark with Noah. After the Flood, dinosaurs apparently were brought to extinction by humans and other pressures. The dinosaur/dragon legends from all over the world support this claim.

9:6 What really happened to the dinosaurs? Ham, www.answersingenesis.org/radio/pdf/whathappenedtodinos.pdf

According to evolutionists, dinosaurs evolved 235 million years ago and dominated the landscape until 65 million years ago when they abruptly and mysteriously died out. According to a biblical perspective, dinosaurs were created on Day 6 of the Creation Week and most became extinct as a result of the Flood described in Genesis. Not all dinosaurs died in the Flood—they would have been among the many kinds of animals on the Ark. Those that got off the Ark have since become extinct. The history of the dinosaurs is not as complex as evolutionists make it out to be. The different views are a result of starting from a different set of assumptions.

While we don't know everything about dinosaurs, we can draw certain conclusions based on the evidence found in fossils. It is always important to note that what we know about the dinosaurs is limited by the evidence and the amount of interpretation that is reasonable.

The presence of dinosaur/dragon legends suggests that man and dinosaurs lived together. The diet and behavior of dinosaurs can be known before the Fall—they were all vegetarians (see Genesis 1:29–30)—but after the Fall many of them must have become carnivores based on tooth marks on bones in the fossil record. Although we can't know everything about the dinosaurs, if we start with the Bible as the accurate history book of the universe, we can come to many reasonable conclusions about their history.

9:7 Swimming with the dinosaurs, Wise, www.answersingenesis. org/docs2006/0308dinosaurs.asp

A recent fossil find in China lays to rest the notion that mammals were small, nocturnal creatures during the "age of reptiles." An 18-inch creature with a two-layer fur coat, beaver-like tail, webbed feet, and the mouth of a seal was found fossilized in Jurassic Period rock dated at 164 million years old. This find pushes back the arrival of large mammaliaforms by 100 million years. This means that mammal-like ancestors had to evolve fur and other mammalian features on land and then evolve to be able to survive in the sea 100 million years earlier than large mammals were supposed to have evolved. The presence of this mammal-like creature, with all of its unique design features, is not a problem in the creation model because it would have been present on earth immediately after creation. The Flood preserved a sample of organisms that lived with one another from the beginning.

9:8 Does this evolutionary claim have any legs? Wise, www. answersingenesis.org/docs2006/0421legs.asp

A snake fossil found in Argentina has added to the scientific debate over whether snakes evolved on land or sea. The fossil has leg structures where its hind legs should be. The location suggests that snakes evolved on land in the evolutionary story. Whether the "legs" were used for crawling or mating cannot be known from the fossil. Many such "vestigial" structures are supposed to show a transition from legged to legless states. A snake with legs fits within the creation model with no need for adjustments. It is possible that this form of snake had legs, which may have been lost due to natural selection (without demonstrating molecules-to-man evolution).

9:9 The evolution of feathers: a major problem for Darwinism,
Bergman, www.answersingenesis.org/tj/v17/i1/feathers.asp

The origin of birds has always been a major problem for Darwinism, and even today little agreement exists about their evolution. One of the most difficult issues related to bird evolution is the evolution of feathers. Feathers are complex, designed structures required for flight, and are today found only on birds. A literature review on the evolution of bird feathers showed that even though feathers are found as far back as the Cretaceous, including many well-preserved samples in amber, the fossil record fails to provide solid evidence for feather evolution. The implications of this major difficulty for Darwinism are discussed in this article.

The presence of feathers for flight has allowed birds to spread to every corner of the globe. Their coloration, songs, and flight make them a marvel of God's creation.

Animal skin types range from a thin structure seen in worms to scaly reptiles, feathered birds, and furry mammals. Each of these skin types performs a different function, and the information is different for each type of structure in the skin. Scales, hair, horns, nails, claws, and feathers are all made of the protein keratin and are outgrowths of the skin. Though they are all made of keratin, they are different forms of keratin.

The structure of a feather is much more complex than it appears. Each feather contains a main shaft, barbs, and barbules on the barbs, which contain many small hooklets and grooves that act like Velcro to hold the feather together. There are over a dozen types of feathers.

The nervous system to control flight is amazingly complex. The complex system of brain, muscles, lungs, tendons, and feathers must have evolved all at once in an irreducibly complex system. Each part by itself would not be likely to provide a survival advantage. The sudden appearance of fully formed feathers in the fossil record supports the idea of special creation.

Many evolutionists hypothesize that feathers actually evolved for insulation and were later exploited for flight by modification. Some disagree with this idea, and it is still contested.

The origin of flight in evolutionary hypotheses ranges from tree-down gliders to ground-up flyers. As there is no evidence for either theory, the speculative debate continues. Feathers and bird bones are relatively abundant in the fossil record, with 79% of the 329 living families known as fossils. No transitional structures between scales, skin, and feathers are known from the fossil record, suggesting birds appeared suddenly—during Day 5 of Creation Week.

The complex differences between reptilian scales and bird feathers mean that a set of intermediate steps would have been needed, none of which are seen in the fossils. A hair-like follicle must have developed, making the evolutionary connection between hair and feathers more plausible. The problem is that this would not fit the other evolutionary evidence; so a story must be imagined to explain the miraculous development. The development from the billows-style lungs of reptiles to the unique features of the birds' respiratory system is another insurmountable problem for Darwinists. The evidence clearly points to the amazing design of the Divine Creator of the Bible.

9:10 Tiny bones—giant assumptions, www.answersingenesis.org/creation/v22/i3/focus.asp

In a blaze of publicity, primate fossil bones found in China were enthusiastically hailed by evolutionists as "the primate equivalent of the missing link." The "dawn monkey," *Eosimias*, was described as being shy, nocturnal, having "large, saucer-like eyes" and spending its life flitting about the treetops of humid Asian rainforests, catching insects, and drinking plant nectar.

And what is the fossil evidence on which this story is based? Nothing more than some tiny fossil foot/ankle bones no bigger than rice grains! It is amazing how far the facts get stretched to accommodate the story of how primates must have evolved.

9:11 How did animals spread all over the world from where the Ark landed? Taylor, www.answersingenesis.org/articles/nab/how-did-animals-spread

In evolutionary thinking, marsupials are restricted mainly to Australia because of their isolation due to the splitting of the continents and their inability to compete with placental mammals in other areas. In the Flood model, animals would have rapidly spread out from the Ark after the Flood. Their migration paths most likely followed preferred food and habitat sources. Some animals went in different directions and established populations. Starting with what is revealed in Genesis, we can know that God intended for the earth to be repopulated after the Flood. The inclusion of pairs of animal kinds on the Ark would have accomplished this with their offspring spreading across the globe and adapting to the local environments through natural selection.

The presence of land bridges during the Ice Age that likely followed the Flood would have allowed animals to migrate to any continent from the Ark's resting place, somewhere near modern Turkey. Populations of marsupials were present in places other than

Did kangaroos once live in the Middle East?

The Ice Age that followed Noah's Flood caused the ocean levels to drop. Land bridges between all of the continents except Antarctica allowed animals (and humans) to spread across the globe and populate different areas. Certain kinds were more successful depending on the climate of a certain region.

Australia but were apparently not able to survive as they competed for food and as the climate changed. Large marsupials with their young in pouches would be able to travel long distances—in effect beating the other mammals to Australia and establishing themselves there. With the Bible as the foundation, distribution of animals after the Flood is not a problem to explain, although the details cannot be fully known and our models must be flexible in light of new evidence.

9:12 The echidna enigma … and the platypus puzzle, Doolan, www.answersingenesis.org/creation/v18/i2/echidna.asp

The echidna (spiny anteater) and platypus belong to the mammalian order Monotremata (monotremes) because of their unique ability to lay eggs. They have the other mammalian characteristics of fur and mammary glands, but they do not give live birth as the marsupial and placental mammals do. Both of the monotremes have a venomous spur on their hind feet. This feature, along with molecular "evidence," has led evolutionists to believe that the monotremes diverged early in mammalian history to form a distinct group. They are often referred to as "primitive," reflecting the evolutionary bias. The lack of any possible ancestors from the fossil record leaves their evolutionary history a complete mystery. Fossil monotremes show no distinct differences from living specimens, giving the appearance that they were created fully formed as described in Genesis and were fossilized as a result of the global Flood of Noah's day.

9:13 The beauty of the peacock tail and the problems with the theory of sexual selection, Burgess, www.answersingenesis.org/tj/v15/i2/peacock.asp

One of the most dramatic and well-known examples of sexual selection occurs in the tail of the peacock. The display feathers come at an extreme cost to the individual male, but females apparently choose the males to mate with based on their plumage. How this mechanism originally developed

The amazing amount of developmental control that is required to produce the patterns in the peacock's tail defies the information-producing limits of mutations. These amazing patterns are evidence of a Creator—they are not an accident.

is an enigma to evolutionists, and the fact that it contains several irreducibly complex systems increases the difficulty of finding an explanation in the evolutionary framework. The fact that the conspicuous nature of many courtship displays makes a male less able to hide and/or avoid predators transforms "survival of the fittest" into "survival of the handsomest." The male that has the most extreme trait (long tails) will pass his genes onto his offspring, which will tend to have the longest tails in the future. How the females select the males is still a mystery to evolutionists and creationists alike. There is no evidence for a correlation between beauty and health or how the simultaneous development of a sexual trait and its preference would have emerged in the evolutionary story.

The feather pattern of the peacock (female peafowl are called peahens) contains many incredible features that defy an evolutionary explanation: all feathers are oriented to a central point, the intricate pattern of "eyes" are uniformly distributed, modified barb structures are in certain parts of the feather, feathers contain only one pigment, feathers produce colors using multiple layers of thin films, and many others.

The "eye" pattern is actually produced by the interaction of many thousands of barbules whose development must be strictly controlled, layering that varies by 1/20,000th of a millimeter. The mathematical accuracy within the pattern of an individual barb and the overall shape of the "eye" pattern defy mere chance and time as a designer. The amount of original information that must be encoded for this type of a pattern clearly points to the hand of the Intelligent Designer.

Although neither creationists nor evolutionists can explain all of the details of development of intricate sexual displays, the belief that a Creator put beautiful traits in creatures makes much more sense than the just-so story that time and chance got together to produce them by accident.

9:14 The extinction wars, Oard, www.answersingenesis.org/home/area/fit/chapter5.asp

Some evolutionists believe that at least 30 major ice ages have occurred over earth's history. Most creationists hold to the view that there was a single ice age in the recent past. Evolutionists attempt to show how mass extinctions occurred on a global scale following the last (or first and only) Ice Age. The explanations include extinction by climate change, extinction by overhunting, or extinction by diseases introduced by humans and their domestic animals. Each of these hypotheses has major problems, and scientists from around the world have been unable to agree on this issue, even after over 100 years of study.

Details within a post-Flood Ice Age model seem to explain the evidence the best, but the Bible is the foundation for such thinking. Therefore, evolutionists must reject the clearest of the interpretations. The problems with the evolutionary models lie in the fact that their basic assumptions do not line up with the true history of the earth described in the Bible.

Questions to Consider

1. Since feathers and reptilian scales develop in fundamentally different ways, why do evolutionists assume that they evolved from the same structure?

2. Do all scientists agree on the pattern of evolutionary development (phylogenetic tree) of vertebrates? How can we know which view of history is true?

3. How do scientists resolve conflicts between cladistic studies and "molecular clock" studies?

4. What type of evidence would scientists accept to suggest that birds did not evolve from dinosaurs, amphibians from fish, reptiles from amphibians, etc.?

5. If it could be demonstrated that amphibians did not evolve from fish, what would happen to the remaining parts of evolutionary theory?

6. Does the fossil of a fish with bony structures in its fin indicate that it was evolving into an amphibian? Are there other alternative explanations for why some fish have fleshy and bony fins, like the living coelacanth?

7. Since feathers and fur both develop from a similar tube structure in the skin, why don't scientists believe that they evolved from one another? How do we decide when it is convergent or divergent evolution?

8. What evidence do scientists use when they describe the lifestyle and particular habits of extinct species? Does this allow for multiple interpretations that seem to fit the data? What are some of these alternatives within evolution?

9. What lines of evidence do scientists use when they claim that dinosaurs had feathers even though no feathers have been found with the fossils? Is this good science?

10. How should the lines in phylogenetic trees be interpreted? Are the branching points based on actual evidence, or are they an

interpretation of what "must have happened" to get to where we are today?

11. Why don't all textbooks and authorities use the same dates for major events in evolutionary history? How do we decide which authority to trust?

Tools for Digging Deeper

(see a complete list in the Introduction)

The New Answers Book 1 & 2 by Ham et al.

The Biotic Message by Walter ReMine

Creation: Facts of Life by Gary Parker

Darwin's Black Box by Michael Behe

Evolution: The Fossils Still Say No! by Duane Gish

Frozen in Time by Michael Oard

If Animals Could Talk by Werner Gitt

In the Beginning Was Information by Werner Gitt

Not by Chance by Lee Spetner

10

THE ORIGIN OF HUMANS

'Biologists would dearly like to know how modern apes, modern humans and the various ancestral hominids have evolved from a common ancestor. Unfortunately, the fossil record is somewhat incomplete as far as the hominids are concerned, and it is all but blank for the apes. The best we can hope for is that more fossils will be found over the next few years which will fill the present gaps in the evidence.' The author goes on to say: 'David Pilbeam [a well-known expert in human evolution] comments wryly, "If you brought in a smart scientist from another discipline and showed him the meagre evidence we've got he'd surely say, 'forget it: there isn't enough to go on'."

—Richard E. Leakey, *The Making of Mankind,*
Michael Joseph Limited, London, 1981, p. 43

What You Will Learn

You have probably seen the famous depiction of a monkey progressively turning into an upright human figure. But what evidence is there for this popular picture? The fossil record that is used to support human evolution has become more and more questionable as more and more fossils are found. The cautious way in which human ancestry is treated in the textbooks is evidence of the lack of consensus in the area of human evolution. What used to be direct evolutionary trees have become overlapping bars on a timeline. Most scientists believe that primates and humans all share a recent common ancestor at about 80 million years ago. This date is not based on fossils but on the similarity in DNA sequences and the assumptions surrounding the use of such "molecular clocks." Many of the fossils of human ancestors consist of little more than fragments of bone, some of which have been exposed as frauds.

Most creationists consider Neanderthals, Cro-Magnon, and some other fossil groups as representatives of extinct people groups, not evolutionary dead ends. Interpretation of fossils from an evolutionary perspective is not compatible with the teachings of the Bible. The fact that chimpanzees and humans have similar DNA does not make them evolutionary relatives. Humans did not evolve in a series of random accidents from an apelike ancestor—they were created in the image of God. The Bible makes a clear distinction between man and the animals. Man is given the ability to fellowship with God and given dominion over the animals. Evolutionary ideas about the rise of man from apes has fueled racist attitudes and set the stage for such atrocities as the Holocaust. Humans were specially created by God and are not simply highly evolved primates.

What Your Textbook Says about the Origin of Humans

Evolutionary Concept	Glencoe	PH-Campbell	PH-Miller	Holt	Articles
Paleoanthropologists study human ancestry and cultures to explain the evolutionary history of humans.	428–435	575–577	140–141	T195, 731–738, T731–T732	1:2, 10:1
Humans and dinosaurs never existed on earth at the same time, contrary to popular beliefs.	—	T575	—	T723	10:2
All primates have a common ancestor from 80 million years ago. Gorillas, orangutans, chimps, and humans belong to the family Hominidae.	420–421, 424, 847, 1068–1069, 1086	574–575, T576	T382, 833–835, T836, 837, T841	731–732, T732, T734, 735, 813	3:6, 3:7, 10:1, 10:3
Similarities in many primate traits mean they share a common ancestor. DNA and fossil evidence can provide the evolutionary history of primates.	423, 427, 436–437	249, 302–304, 344, 574, 577	833, 835	220, 232, 732, 733, T733, 737–738, T737, 742–743	3:6, 3:7, 10:1, 10:3
Humans are evolved from hominids evident in the fossil record from 7 million years ago.	367, 425, 426	575–576	434, 835–839, T838	733–734	10:1, 10:3
Homo sapiens appeared in Africa 200,000 years ago based on fossil and DNA evidence.	379, 433	577	434, 839–840, T840	737	10:1, 10:3

Evolutionary Concept	Glencoe	PH-Campbell	PH-Miller	Holt	Articles
Humans, chimps, and gorillas share an ancestor within 8 million years ago. Humans are most closely related to chimps with only a 2–5% difference in their DNA.	428	304, 575	835	T198, 732, T732, 735	3:6, 10:4, 10:5
Australopithecines are the most likely ancestors of humans. "Lucy" is a fossil of *Australopithecus afarensis* that demonstrates upright walking and human features 3.2 million years ago.	430–431	575–576	387, 836	733	10:1, 10:3
Homo habilis and *Homo erectus* are extinct along the evolutionary path to *Homo sapiens*. The exact evolutionary path of hominids is not clear from the fossil record, but trends are clearly present.	431, 435	576	T838, 839–840	734–736	10:1, 10:3
Neanderthals coexisted with modern humans and were an evolutionary dead end that left no descendants.	434	577	T836, T839, 841	738	10:1, 10:3, 10:6

Note: Page numbers preceded by "T" indicate items from the teacher notes found in the margins of the Teacher's Edition.

What We Really Know about the Origin of Humans

The origin of humans is most certainly one of the most contentious points of evolutionary theory. Many people who believe in the God of the Bible accept that evolution created the animals but they still believe that humans (or at least their souls) were created by God. Such compromise positions have ultimately undermined the authority of God's Word; Scripture is accepted for its moral value but not for its absolute truth in every area. It would seem that almost every culture on the planet has some story to explain how humans came to be. Many of these involve supernatural acts by gods. Naturalistic science, by its own definition, does not accept these supernatural events and regards them as myth. Religion and mythology are often viewed as some evolved coping mechanism to explain things that our brains have not been able to understand or directly experience. The scientific community must reject a supernatural origin based on its naturalistic/materialistic definition of science.

One of the reasons that human evolution is such a hot issue in Western culture stems from the direct conflict it has with biblical Christianity. In the creation account of Genesis 1 and 2, man is created in a position above the animals—in the very "image of God." In evolutionary philosophy, man is a mere accident in the experiment run by time, chance, and natural laws. Man occupies no more important a position in the universe than does an asteroid floating through space. This notion runs contrary to the emotions of most people, but that may simply be arrogance due to our highly evolved brains.

Many may believe that there is a wide array of fossil evidence that clearly shows how apes have become humans. The iconic depiction of a hunched monkey gradually developing into an upright-walking human has been viewed by most people. The problem is that much of the visuals are made up. The absence of a consistent story of evolution is obvious in the way that human ancestry is presented in the textbooks. Instead of showing a phylogenetic tree, two of the textbooks (Holt and PH-Campbell) simply show timelines representing the fossils. The Glencoe text shows a "possible" phylogenetic tree with many dashed lines (which are assumed to

When the phrase "human evolution" is used, this is probably one of the first images to pop into people's minds. Despite its iconic status and widespread use, it is not based on factual evidence, but on imagination.

be questionable, even though they are not indicated as such), and one line appearing out of thin air. The cautious treatment of this topic shows the lack of consensus within the scientific community regarding the alleged ancestry of humans.

The proposed evolutionary ancestors to humans have changed many times over the decades as new fossil evidence has been gathered. While it is not expected that theories should remain constant, the picture seems to become less and less common with the addition of new information. Many nearly identical terms are used to describe alleged human and ape ancestors. Care must be taken to distinguish between hominoids, humanoids, hominins, hominans, and hominids. The most commonly discussed term is "hominid":

Hominid: extinct and living members of the family Hominidae, including modern humans and their ancestors.

The term hominid has a somewhat contradictory definition within and between the textbooks reviewed. Different classification schemes place the orangutans, gorillas, and chimps (these three are commonly called the "great apes") in the family Pongidae, while other schemes place these three in the family Hominidae with humans. Depending on which scheme is used for classification, the meaning of the word changes. Whether the term includes the great apes is somewhat irrelevant in that all groups still share a supposed common ancestor. In the broader scope, all four of these groups would be referred to as hominoids. The textbooks seem to indicate that only bipedal (walking upright on two legs) primates are classified as hominids, and the figures discussing hominids include "ancestors" that are assumed to be bipedal (*Homo*, *Australopithecus*, *Ardipithecus*, etc.). A review of current literature seems to indicate a trend toward including all four groups in the family Hominidae, which would mean the definition would need to be modified. The term has no value in the creationist model because there are no human ancestors—apes are apes, humans are humans. This does not mean that all creationists agree on the classification of all of the fossil primates. Classification is a subjective issue, especially when dealing in the historical realm of fossils and fragments of fossils. It is important to recognize the limits of accuracy when dealing with such a topic.

Many evolutionists try to dispel the popular idea that humans evolved from monkeys. While that statement is a simplification of human evolution, evolutionists claim that there is a common ancestor for monkeys, apes, and humans. If this common ancestor didn't look something like a monkey, what did it look like? It would be more accurate to say that humans, monkeys, and apes have a common ancestor, but the distinction is relatively minor when considering that the ancestor of all apes and monkeys must have looked something like an ape or monkey.

Many evolutionists complain when people say that humans descended from monkeys. If the common ancestor for chimpanzees and humans shown in this phylogenetic tree did not look like a monkey, what did it look like?

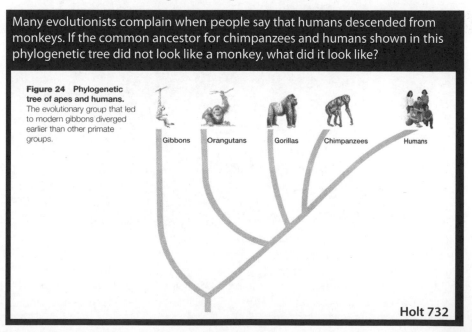

Figure 24 **Phylogenetic tree of apes and humans.** The evolutionary group that led to modern gibbons diverged earlier than other primate groups.

Gibbons   Orangutans   Gorillas   Chimpanzees   Humans

Holt 732

The moral implications of the evolutionary philosophy that man is simply an advanced ape are increasingly manifested in our culture. If man is an ape, then the apelike or "primal" urges that we have for violence and sexuality can be excused as coming from our evolutionary history. Exercising those urges is contrary to the Christian doctrine of self-control. Many evolutionists try to separate biological evolution from evolutionary-based social philosophies on the grounds that those philosophies are not scientific. While this is true, evolutionists still try to deal with questions of behavior and their origins.

Bioethics is the area that deals with the moral and ethical implications of scientific knowledge and the technology it produces. If society espouses evolutionary/materialistic beliefs, those beliefs have consequences. There is no absolute basis for morality in a materialistic belief system; right and wrong are determined by the individual and society. As society changes, the laws that govern a society also change. Accepting the view that humans are simply

The social concept of relative morality is based on evolutionary doctrine. If man is a product of random, cosmic accidents, then man should be able to decide what is right and wrong (if right and wrong even exist in humanistic philosophy). The problem is that there is no basis for deciding what point of view is right or wrong if each person comes to a different conclusion. The Bible provides absolute truth and authority for making moral decisions.

highly evolved apes and that man determines truth is directly contrary to the absolute authority of the Creator God of the Bible.

Starting from the evolutionary bias that apes and humans are similar, some evolutionists have proposed that chimps should actually be reclassified in the genus *Homo* alongside humans. Taking this a step further, several groups are pushing for "human rights" for the apes. If they are truly that similar to us, why not grant them these rights? One reason is that the Bible makes a clear distinction between human life and the life of animals. We are to be stewards of the earth and have dominion over the animals, but we are created in the image of God, which makes us distinct from the apes.

An examination of the fossils that are proposed as human ancestors, or at least along the branch that led to humans, shows many specimens that overlap in evolutionary time, as well as gaps of millions of years. There is no consensus on the path to humans, and any representation of the lineage is highly subjective. In the biblical creationist model, these specimens either represent some type of extinct ape, or groups of humans.

One of the unfortunate elements of the acceptance of the evolutionary origins of man was a marked increase in racial prejudice. Although racism certainly existed before the 1850s, evolution gave white Europeans a "scientific" justification to dominate the "less evolved" Africans and Australian Aborigines. Australian Aborigines were actually killed and taken to London as museum specimens of the "missing link" between apemen and modern humans. A pygmy by the name of Ota Benga was placed on exhibit in the monkey house at the Bronx Zoo. What could justify such treatment of humans? Evolution was used to justify the display because the Africans, Aborigines, and Mongols (Asians) were arbitrarily considered inferior races to the Caucasians of Europe. In contrast, the Bible explains that all men are created in the image of God (Genesis 1:26–27) and are of one blood (Acts 17:26)—there are no inferior races. In fact, there is only one race, the human race.

Humans are humans and have been so since the beginning; no prehistoric hominids ever evolved into humans. Though the fossil record is incomplete, it can only be interpreted accurately if the presuppositions are true—that truth comes from God, who is the only eyewitness to all of the events of history.

Many textbooks have avoided including a tree of human evolution because the interpretation of fossil hominids changes constantly. This set of overlapping bars is actually a more accurate picture of the existence of distinct groups that have existed in the past. The time scale used directly contradicts the Bible, and many of the distinct groups are likely members of a single genus that has been artificially split based on evolutionary assumptions.

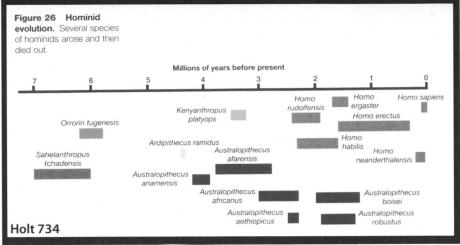

Figure 26 Hominid evolution. Several species of hominids arose and then died out.

Millions of years before present

Holt 734

Reference Articles

10:1 Did humans really evolve from apelike creatures? Menton, preview at www.answersingenesis.org/home/area/wow/preview/part4.asp

Many popular magazines and television programs show evidence purportedly proving that humans evolved from an apelike ancestor. Is the evidence real, or are they making apes out of men and men out of apes? Starting from biblical assumptions, we see clearly that God made man in His image and did not use evolution. Some Christians who accept evolution say that man's soul was created by God, but evolution made the physical form. The evolutionary assumptions demand that man evolved from an apelike ancestor and discount biblical authority. Paleoanthropologists don't ask *if* man evolved from apes, but *which* apes he evolved from.

The fossil evidence of hominids (alleged human ancestors) is extremely limited, and very few people actually get to see the actual fossils. Most studies are done from casts of the fossils or pictures. And because jaws and teeth are the most commonly preserved primate fossils, these become a key part of the interpretations. The fraudulent Nebraska Man, including his family and livestock, was identified and drawn based on a single tooth, which was later found to be from an extinct pig.

Skull anatomy is also important, since brain capacity and facial features are used to demonstrate the supposed human-like features in some ape fossils. Leg and hip bones are important in demonstrating how the hominids walked. Those that walked upright are more human than those that didn't.

To make an apelike human ancestor appear out of the fossil record, paleoanthropologists do one of three things. First, they combine pieces from an ape fossil and a human fossil and call it a hominid ancestor. This happened in the case of Piltdown man, which was identified as a hoax after being promoted as man's ancestor for 50 years. The second way is to emphasize the ape features of a human fossil, such as oversized jaws, sloping foreheads, and other features that are found within the range of human variation. Finally, they emphasize the human features on an ape fossil. This is evident in the fossil "Lucy," an *Australopithecus afarensis* specimen. Even though *A. afarensis* hips don't support the idea that they walked upright and the foot bones are curved like an ape's, it is usually shown standing with human feet—a blatant misrepresentation of the fossil evidence.

10:2 Australia's Aborigines … did they see dinosaurs? Driver, www.answersingenesis.org/creation/v21/i1/aborigines.asp

Stories of large creatures have been present in modern cultures around the world. Some of the most popular include Mokele-Mbembe and the Loch Ness Monster. While evolutionists must dismiss all of these claims as absurd because dinosaurs have been extinct for 65 million years, there is no reason to doubt that some species of dinosaurs could have

Problem-Solving Lab 16.2

Apply Concepts

How similar are Neandertals and humans? Fossil evidence can provide clues to similarities and differences between Neandertals and humans.

Solve the Problem

Examine the diagram of a human skull superimposed on a Neandertal skull. The cranial capacities (brain size) of the two skulls are provided.

1450 cm³

1600 cm³

Brow-
ridge

— Neandertal
▢ Modern human

Thinking Critically

1. **Measure** How much larger is a Neandertal brain than a human brain? Express the value as a percentage.
2. **Interpret Scientific Illustrations** Which skull has the more protruding jaw? A thicker browridge? Are a protruding jaw and thick browridges more apelike or humanlike characteristics? Explain your judgment.
3. **Identify** What clues do fossils such as spear points and hand axes, shelters made of animal skins, and flowers and animal horns at burial sites provide about the lifestyle of Neandertals?

Glencoe 433

In this activity, the features that are more apelike are emphasized to distinguish modern human skulls from Neanderthals. Despite the larger brain capacity and the features that can be found in the modern-day human population, Neanderthals are demoted to a sub-human category. Many scientists are beginning to reexamine the Neanderthal evidence and are using disease and diet to explain some of the skeletal differences seen.

survived the 4,500 years since the Flood. Credible accounts of the "bunyip," "burrunjor," and "kulta" among Aborigines seem to fit descriptions of "prehistoric" dinosaur-like creatures that could have survived in remote regions.

The evidence of human and dinosaur coexistence includes cave paintings that apparently depict dinosaurs, the mention of dragons and behemoth in the Bible, and the presence of many dinosaur and dragon descriptions and pictures in Europe and Asia.

10:3 Human Beings, Parker, www.answersingenesis.org/cec/docs/cfl-pdfs.asp

Humans are the result of either a cosmic accident orchestrated by time and chance or the special creative act of God. Evolutionists once viewed Neanderthals as dumb, cave-dwelling brutes that were less than human, but creationists have always argued that they were fully human. Neanderthals lived in very harsh conditions where disease and nutrition may have produced some of the skeletal features seen, and many evolutionists are beginning to accept the creationist view of Neanderthals as an extinct human people group—not a missing link.

Tragically, other human people groups have been considered missing links and treated in barbaric ways. African Negroes and Australian Aborigines were sometimes considered less evolved humans. A century ago, Darwin's idea encouraged the slaughter of Aborigines, and some were even prepared as museum specimens. It also gave credence to Hitler's plan to exterminate the "inferior" Jewish race.

Piltdown man was thought to be a missing link for over 50 years before it was discovered to be a fraudulent combination of a human skull and an orangutan jaw. But because people wanted to believe evolution, they initially accepted the evidence without scientific scrutiny. The many different and dubious interpretations of Java man and Peking man (well documented in *Bones of Contention* by Martin Lubenow) are further evidence that people see what they believe in the fossils. Nebraska man was a hallmark in the Scopes Trial, but the tooth that inspired this image was later determined to be from an extinct pig.

There is no need to look for missing links if man is classified as a monkey, as a 1993 display at the Australian National Museum depicted: the common

> Despite the claim that australopithecines like Lucy walked upright, the data does not support the claim. Other apes living today have similar leg structures and do not walk upright.

Holt 733

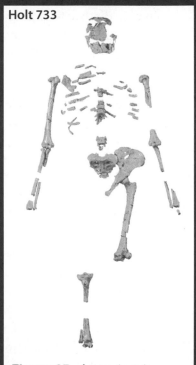

Figure 25   Lucy. Lucy's leg bones indicate that she walked upright. She stood about 1 m (3 ft) tall.

behaviors in humans and various apes were set forward as evidence for the claim.

Australopithecus, the genus of the infamous "Lucy" specimen, is one of the most cited examples of a missing link in human evolution. The problem is that australopithecine features are all apelike, despite the claim that they walked upright. Many depictions actually show human hands and feet when the evidence clearly indicates curved, apelike features.

The fact that tools are found with some australopithecine fossils and that human fossils are found in strata directly underneath suggests that the tools may have been used on the apes, not by them. The extinct ape fossils may share characteristics with modern humans, but so do living apes. No evidence from the fossil record directly supports a transitional series from ape to human. Virtually every major discovery is later reinterpreted to fit a new version of evolution. People have always been people and apes have always been apes. Each was created according to the purpose and plan of God.

10:4 Chimp-human hybridization: two of a kind or two different kinds? DeWitt, www.answersingenesis.org/docs2006/0531chimp.asp

In a complicated twisting of the evolutionary history of humans and chimps, a group of scientists studying hominoid DNA sequences has proposed a radical chain of events. Nick Patterson and his colleagues make the suggestion that chimps and humans began to diverge about 10 million years ago. Then, about 6 million years ago, they believe the two distinct populations merged to form a group of hybrids. They believe that fertile hybrid females then crossed back to one of the ancestral species, subsequently giving rise to distinct human and chimpanzee species. This extreme view is based on the fact that different regions of DNA sequence give different dates for divergence. There are also regions of the DNA where humans are closer to gorillas than humans and chimps. Instead of questioning the validity of the dating techniques, a contorted explanation is developed. The explanation of the data demonstrates the plastic nature of the evolutionary models. The differences are not expected in the Darwinian interpretation, but they fit the idea that each kind was created to be unique. Man and apes should not be considered to be closely related—as the data clearly suggests.

10:5 Chimp genome sequence very different from man, DeWitt, www.answersingenesis.org/go/dna-chimp

Evolutionists have claimed that chimp and human DNA is up to 99% similar. These studies only looked at gene coding regions, which are a tiny fraction of the 3 billion base pairs in the human genome. When the chimp genome was sequenced, the number was reduced to 96%, twice as much difference as was previously thought. No matter what the difference, evolution would predict it, and evolutionists would claim it as proof. It is estimated that 40 million mutation events would be required to produce 125 million differences in the DNA sequences. There's not enough time in the evolutionary explanation for this to happen (Haldane's Dilemma), and no new information is generated in these types of mutations anyway.

Some scientists are surprised at the anatomical, physical, and behavioral differences between man and chimpanzee when they see so much apparent genetic similarity. With a philosophy that excludes a Creator God, they are forced to accept similarity as evidence of common ancestry. However, similarity can also be the result of a common Designer. The differences make the difference, and the most important difference is that man is created in the image of God.

10:6 Neandertal Man—the changing picture, Oard, www.answersingenesis.org/creation/v25/i4/neandertal.asp

Neanderthals are often portrayed as unintelligent cavemen in animal-skin clothing. Neanderthals were

The idea that skeletal features of australopithecines are intermediate to humans and chimpanzees is an interpretation that comes from the assumption that chimps and humans have a common ancestor. Starting from a different assumption, that humans and chimps have a common Designer, the evidence points to a Creator using similar structures to perform similar functions.

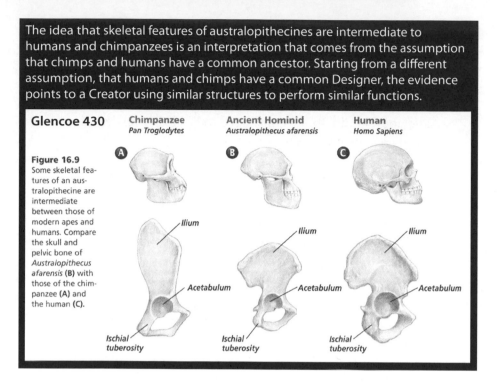

Glencoe 430

| Chimpanzee | Ancient Hominid | Human |
| *Pan Troglodytes* | *Australopithecus afarensis* | *Homo Sapiens* |

Figure 16.9
Some skeletal features of an australopithecine are intermediate between those of modern apes and humans. Compare the skull and pelvic bone of *Australopithecus afarensis* (**B**) with those of the chimpanzee (**A**) and the human (**C**).

first thought to be subhuman, but that thought is beginning to change. In the creationist view, Neanderthals and Cro-Magnons were post-Flood people groups that resulted after the dispersion from Babel. Neanderthals were originally given the name *Homo neanderthalensis* and considered an ancestor to modern humans. Forty-four years after this biased classification, Neanderthals were reclassified as a human subspecies *Homo sapiens neanderthalensis* and described as nearly human. It has been claimed that they were unintelligent even though their brain capacity was larger than modern humans, and interpretations of their social habits vary from hunter to vegetarian.

Neanderthals present a challenge to Christians who believe that soulless humans came before Adam. There is conclusive evidence that Neanderthals and humans lived at the same time. Recent discoveries of a human-like hyoid bone, burial practices, musical instruments, weapons, and other signs of culture have started to shift the picture in even the evolutionists' minds. Evidence of hybridization between humans and Neanderthals, DNA comparisons, and the indications that they lived together for 100,000 years of evolutionary time point to the fact that they were fully human. This evidence contradicts evolutionary assumptions and supports the biblical position that Neanderthals simply represent some of the variety that was programmed into the human genome by our Creator.

Questions to Consider

1. Since a species is commonly defined as a group that can inter-breed, it seems that fossils could never be identified to the species level because we can't observe how they interbreed. How do scientists determine what species a fossil is if it looks similar to another fossil but is a different size or slightly different shape?

2. When scientists disagree with the classification of a fossil, who decides where it belongs?

3. Since bananas share about 50% of their DNA with humans, does that mean bananas are half human?

4. Does the suggestion that chimpanzee and human DNA are similar necessarily mean that they had a common ancestor? Could it also be considered evidence for a common designer?

5. Since the human-chimp DNA comparisons are only based on a comparison of part of the genomes, how can it be claimed that they are 96% similar?

6. Are there any alternative scientific explanations for humans evolving from apelike creatures?

7. How do paleontologists know that certain apelike creatures were evolutionary dead ends and others led to a new species? Are there multiple ways to interpret the evidence? How do we know which to trust?

8. If it is inaccurate to say that humans evolved from apes, but instead we should say all apes and humans have a common ancestor, what did the ancestor look like if not like an ape?

9. Scientists often deal with bioethical issues (cloning, genetically modified foods, drugs, etc.). If man has evolved from apes, what is the moral basis for deciding what is right and wrong? If cultures determine what is right, how can we claim that other cultures' views are wrong? If terrorists act within their beliefs and Nazis believe they are superior, can we say that they are wrong? Would Nazi ideology be right if it was accepted by a majority of cultures?

10. Why has the picture of human evolution become less clear as more and more fossils have been found? It would seem that the picture would become clearer with more information.

11. When we look at a car or an airplane, it is only logical to suggest that it was designed with the features that it has. The human body is much more intricate and complex than the most complex machines we can design. Why is it considered illogical to consider that the human body has a designer?

Tools for Digging Deeper

(see a complete list in the Introduction)

The New Answers Book 1 & 2 by Ham et al.

Bones of Contention by Marvin Lubenow

Buried Alive by Jack Cuozzo

Creation: Facts of Life by Gary Parker

The Fossil Book by Gary Parker

www.answersingenesis.org/go/genetics

abiogenesis: the alleged spontaneous generation of living organisms from non-living matter

adaptation: a physical trait or behavior due to inherited characteristics that gives an organism the ability to survive in a given environment

adaptive radiation: the process of speciation as populations spread and encounter different environments

allele: any of the alternative forms of a gene that occur at a specific spot (locus) in the DNA sequence (genome) of an organism

anthropic principle: life in our universe requires physical constants, laws, and properties that fall within certain narrow ranges; the universe appears designed to support life

anthropology: systematic study of the characteristics of humans through history

archaebacteria: the kingdom of prokaryotic cells, excluding eubacteria (considered as a separate domain in certain classification schemes), which is alleged to be ancestral to eubacteria by some evolutionists

Archaeopteryx: extinct species of perching bird (known from fossils) with teeth, wing claws, and a bony tail

Archaeoraptor: a fraudulent fossil from China that combined the body of a bird with the tail of a dinosaur

artifact: an item or its remains produced in the past by humans; generally recovered through archaeological exploration

atheism: the belief that God, or any supreme intelligence, does not exist

Australopithecus: genus of extinct apes known from fossils found in Africa, including the famous "Lucy"

bacteria: a group of unicellular organisms that lack a true nucleus and membrane-bound organelles; including eubacteria and archaebacteria

baramin: (see created kind)

Bible: the collection of 66 books that is the inspired Word of God; used as the authoritative source for determining truth

biblical creation: the supernatural events, occurring over six approximately 24-hour days, described in Genesis 1 and 2, by which God caused the formation of the heaven amd earth and everything in them

biblical creation model: a scientific model based on the biblical account of three key events—creation, the curse of nature brought about by Adam's sin, and the global catastrophe of Noah's Flood

big bang model: the cosmological model suggesting the universe began as a single point which expanded to produce the known universe

biology: the systematic study of the characteristics and interactions of living things

beneficial mutation: a mutation which confers a survival advantage to an organism under certain environmental conditions; usually a result of the loss of genetic information (see mutation)

catastrophism: the doctrine that changes in the geologic record are a result of physical processes operating at rates that are dramatically higher than are observed today

cell theory: a theory of biology consisting of three parts: (1) cells are the basic unit of all living things; (2) all living things are composed of one or more cells; and (3) all cells come from preexisting cells

chemistry: the systematic study of the properties and interaction of matter

clone: an organism that is genetically identical to its parent

cloning: producing a new organism using the DNA of an existing organism

cosmogony: a belief about the origin of the universe

cosmology: the systematic study of the structure of the universe, including its origin

created kind (baramin): the original organisms (and their descendants) created supernaturally by God as described in Genesis 1; these organisms reproduce only their own kind within the limits of preprogrammed information, but with great variation

Note: Since the original creation, organisms of one kind cannot inter-breed with a different kind, but individuals within a kind may have lost the ability (information) to interbreed due to the effects of the Curse.

Cro-Magnon man: an extinct people group of Europe and Eastern Asia

Darwinism: a belief that all organisms have a single common ancestor that has produced all living organisms through the process of natural selection; popu-larized by Charles Darwin in *On the Origin of Species*

day-age theory: a compromise belief that the days of Genesis 1 are actually vast ages of different lengths; based on secular dating methods

deism: a belief in a Creator God that denies His intervention in the history of the universe since its creation

DNA (deoxyribonucleic acid): the basic molecule of hereditary information which serves as a code for the production of proteins and is common to all living organisms

endosymbiont hypothesis: the suggestion that mitochondria, chloroplasts, and other organelles originated as bacteria that were ingested and became a part of eukaryotic cells over evolutionary time

entropy (thermodynamics): the measure of the tendency of closed systems to increase in disorder

eubacteria: the kingdom of prokaryotic cells, excluding archaebacteria (consid-ered as a separate domain in certain classification schemes); alleged to be descended from archaebacteria by some evolutionists

evolution: all life on earth has come about through descent with modification from a single common ancestor (a hypothetical, primitive single-celled organism)

extrapolation: inferring information outside of the range of the actual data based on trends

faith: belief in things that cannot be directly known or observed

Flood (Noah's Flood): the supernatural event described in Genesis 6–10 that covered the entire earth with water, killing all land-dwelling, air-breathing animals except those aboard the Ark built by Noah

fossil: preserved remains or traces of once-living organisms

coprolite: fossilized excrement

included fossils: organisms that are encased in a substance leaving the specimen virtually intact, as in amber

living fossils: living organisms that are virtually identical to fossil organisms; often thought to have been extinct and then discovered

mold and cast fossil: a type of replacement fossil which includes the concave or convex impression of an organism; typical of shells and leaves

permineralized fossil: an organism in which the porous parts are filled with mineral deposits leaving the original superstructure intact

replacement (mineralized) fossil: organism whose entire structure has been replaced by mineral deposits so that none of the original superstructure remains

trace/track/micro fossil: evidence of the activity of an organism, including tracks, burrows, root traces

fossilization: the process of preserving the remains or traces of an organism, generally by some form of petrification

gene: a segment of DNA that codes for the production of polypeptides

gene pool: the collection of varying alleles within a population of organisms

genetics: the study of characteristics inherited by the transmission of DNA from parent to offspring

genome: the complete set of genetic material (DNA) of any cell in an organism

geocentric: using the earth as a central frame of reference

geologic column: the layers of rock that compose the crust of the earth

half-life: the amount of time required for one half of the atoms of the parent isotope to decay into the daughter isotope

heliocentric: using the sun as a central frame of reference

heredity: acquiring traits by transfer of genes from parent to offspring

historical (origins) science: interpreting evidence from past events based on a presupposed philosophical point of view

historical theory: an explanation of past events based on the interpretation of evidence that is available in the present

hominid: extinct and living members of the family Hominidae, including modern humans and their ancestors

Homo erectus: fossils of extinct human people groups that are misinterpreted as missing links in human evolution

Homo habilis: an invalid category consisting of various ape and human fossil fragments

homologous structure: any feature that shares a common design with a similar feature in another species of organism (alleged to support common ancestry in evolutionary models)

Homo sapiens: the category that includes modern humans, Neanderthals, and other extinct human groups

human: any member of the species *Homo sapiens*

humanism: a belief in mankind as the measure of all things; based on relative truth and morality and rejecting any supernatural authority

Ice Age: the period of glaciation following Noah's Flood during which a significant portion of the earth had a cold climate

information: an encoded, symbolically represented message conveying expected action and intended purpose

interpolation: inferring information within the range of the actual data based on trends

Java man: the first fossil specimen of *Homo erectus*

Kennewick man: human remains found in Washington State in 1996

kind (see created kind)

life (biological): anything that contains genetic information, can reproduce off-spring that resemble itself, grows and develops, controls cellular organization and conditions including metabolism and homeostasis, and responds to its environment

Note: The Bible defines life in a different sense, using the Hebrew phrase *nephesh chayyah,* indicating organisms with a life spirit.

logic: systematic application of principles of reasoning to arrive at a conclusion

Lucy: a 40% complete fossil specimen of *Australopithecus afarensis* discovered in Ethiopia in 1974 by Donald Johanson

macroevolution: term used by evolutionists to describe the alleged, unobservable change of one kind of organism to another by natural selection acting on the accumulation of mutations over vast periods of time

mammal: any organism that has fur and nurses young from mammary glands

materialism: a belief claiming that physical matter is the only or fundamental reality and that all organisms, processes, and phenomena can be explained as manifestations or interactions of matter

metamorphic rocks: rocks that have been altered in texture or composition by heat, pressure, or chemical activity after they initially formed

microevolution: term used by evolutionists to describe relatively small changes in genetic variation that can be observed in populations

mineralization: replacement of material from an object, usually organic, with minerals that harden

mitochondrial DNA (mtDNA): small circular loops of DNA found in the mito-chondria of eukaryotic cells

mitochondrial Eve: the most recent common ancestor of humans whose lineage can be traced backward through female ancestors; alleged support for the out-of-Africa hypothesis of human evolution

model: physical, mental, or mathematical representations that can be used to explain observed phenomena and make specific, useful predictions

Mungo man: fossil human remains from Australia dated by evolutionists to 40,000 years or more

mutation: any change in the sequence of DNA base pairs in the genome of an organism

frameshift mutation: addition or deletion of one or more nucleotide pairs in the coding region of a gene causing the triplet codons to be read in the wrong frame

deletion mutation: removal of one or more nucleotide pairs in the DNA sequence

duplication mutation: large segments of DNA that have been copied and inserted into a new position in the DNA sequence, possibly on different chromosomes

insertion mutation: addition of one or more nucleotide pairs in the DNA sequence

inversion mutation: a section of DNA that has been reversed within the chromosome

neutral mutation: any mutation that does not effect the function of an organism

point mutation: addition, deletion, or substitution of a single nucleotide pair in the DNA sequence

translocation mutation: the movement of a section of a chromosome from one position to another, generally between different chromosomes

natural selection: the process by which individuals possessing a set of traits that confer a survival advantage in a given environment tend to leave more off-spring on average that survive to reproduce in the next generation

naturalism: a belief denying that an event or object has a supernatural significance; specifically, the doctrine that scientific laws are adequate to account for all phenomena

Neanderthal/Neandertal: an extinct human people group with relatively thick bones and a distinct culture; disease and nutritional deficiency may be responsible for the bone characteristics

neo-Darwinism: an extension of Darwinism, which includes modern genetic concepts to explain the origin of all life on earth from a single common ancestor

Noah's Flood: (see Flood)

operational (observational) science: a systematic approach to understanding that uses observable, testable, repeatable, and falsifiable experimentation to understand how nature commonly behaves

operational theory: an explanation of a set of facts based on a broad set of repeatable and testable observations that is generally accepted within a group of scientists

organism: any cell or group of cells that exhibits the properties of life (living things) (see life)

paleontology: the systematic study of the history of life on the earth based on the fossil record

permineralization: the filling of cavities of an object, usually organic, with minerals, which harden

petrification: processes, including mineralization, permineralization, and inclusion, which change an object, usually organic, into stone or a similar mineral structure

phylogenetic tree: diagrams that show the alleged evolutionary relationships between organisms

Piltdown man: fraudulent "prehuman" fossil consisting of the skull cap of a modern human and the jaw and teeth of an orangutan

plate tectonics: the systematic study of the movement of the plates that make up the earth's crust

    uniformitarian model: based on the gradual movement of the plates over hundreds of millions of years

    catastrophic model: based on rapid movement of the plates associated with Noah's Flood

polypeptide: a chain of amino acids formed from the DNA template and modified to produce proteins

presupposition: a belief that is accepted as true and is foundational to one's worldview

progressive creation: a compromise belief accepting that God has created organisms in a progressive manner over billions of years to accommodate secular dating methods

punctuated equilibrium: an evolutionary model that suggests evolution occurs in rapid spurts rather than by gradual change

radioactive decay: the breakdown of unstable nuclei of atoms releasing energy and subatomic particles

radiometric dating: using ratios of isotopes produced in radioactive decay to calculate an age of the specimen based on assumed rates of decay and other assumptions

parent isotope: original isotope before it has undergone radioactive decay

daughter isotope: isotope resulting from radioactive decay

half-life: the amount of time required for one half of the parent atoms to decay into the daughter atoms

relative dating: estimating the age of a fossil or rock layer by comparing its position to layers of known age

absolute dating: using radiometric dating to test a specimen in an attempt to estimate its age

religion: a cause, principle, or belief system held to with zeal and conviction

RNA (ribonucleic acid): a molecule found in all living things that serves various roles in producing proteins from the coded information in the DNA sequence

secular: not from a religious perspective or source

secular humanism: (see humanism)

science: the systematic study of a subject in order to gain information (see also operational science and historical science)

speciation: the process of change in a population that produces distinct populations which rarely naturally interbreed due to geographic isolation or other factors

species: a group of organisms within a genus that naturally reproduce and have fertile offspring

spontaneous generation: the false belief that life can arise from nonliving matter

strata: layers of rock deposited by geologic events

theory: (see historical theory and operational theory)

transitions/transitional forms: species that exhibit traits that may be interpreted as intermediate between two kinds of organisms in an evolutionary framework (e.g., an organism with a fish body and amphibian legs)

uniformitarianism: the doctrine that present-day processes acting at similar rates as observed today account for the change evident in the geologic record

vestigial organ: any organ that has a demonstrated reduction and/or loss of function

Note: Vestigial organs include eyes in blind cave-fish but not organs that are assumed to have had a different function in an unknown ancestor.

virus: a nonliving collection of proteins and genetic material that can only reproduce inside of a living cell

Y-chromosome Adam: the most recent common ancestor whose lineage can be traced backwards through male ancestors

INDEX TO CHAPTER & UNIT REVIEW QUESTIONS

The questions indicated below are found at the end of chapters in each textbook and are based on evolutionary concepts or expect answers based on evolutionary ideas. See the Introduction for suggestions on how to respond to these questions.

Glencoe Biology: The Dynamics of Life

Page #	Review Question Number
390–391	5, 11, 13, 14, 15, 18, 19, 21, 23
418–419	8, 9, 11, 12, 13, 14, 15, 17, 21, 22, 23, 24
464	3, 5, 7

Page #	Review Question Number
471	11, 12, 13, 14, 15, 17, 18
575	14, 18, 19, 20
814	10
838	12, 13
856	12

Prentice Hall Biology (Campbell)

Page #	Review Question Number
20	20
320–321	7, 8, 9, 12, 18, 19
350–351	2, 3, 4, 6, 10, 11, 12, 13, 14, 16, 18, 19, 20, 22, 25
376–377	1, 7, 10, 20
398–399	7, 17, 23, 25
438–439	9, 10, 17, 18

Page #	Review Question Number
456	1
472	17
520–521	13, 14, 22
538–539	9, 23
556–557	5, 6, 15, 23
580–581	2, 6, 7, 8, 10, 11, 16, 19, 26

Prentice Hall Biology (Miller)

Page #	Review Question Number
389–390	7, 9, 10, 11, 13, 14, 16, 20, 21, 22, 23, 24, 25, 26, 27, 28, 31, 33, 34, 35
391	4, 5, 7, 8
413–414	10, 16, 22, 23, 24, 30, 33
442–444	3, 5, 6, 8-3
445	1-8
464–466	6, 7, 12, 15, 16, 17, 18, 19, 20, 21, 27, 32, 33, 34
467	2, 5, 8
545–546	21, 25, 30, 32
574–576	2, 12, 18
630	34

Page #	Review Question Number
651–652	20, 26
711	26
741	20
760–762	1, 2, 12, 18, 22, 28, 31, 33, 35
763	2
792–794	3, 13, 21, 30, 32, 33
816–818	2, 12, 13, 15, 16, 22, 24, 35
819	2
844–846	2, 11, 14, 18, 21, 23, 25, 26, 27, 30, 33, 36, 37
847	3, 8, 9, 10
866–868	12, 14, 29
869	8, 9, 10

Holt Biology

Page #	Review Question Number
22	7
23	5
156	13
270	2, 3, 4, 5, 6, 9, 10, 11, 12, 13, 15
271	1, 3, 4, 5, 6
294	1, 2, 3, 5, 6, 8, 10, 11, 12, 13, 14, 15
295	2, 5, 6, 7
312	7, 8, 9, 10, 11, 12
313	3, 4, 6, 7
334	6
335	5, 8
380	1
452	8, 11

Page #	Review Question Number
476	1
524	1, 12
525	1
612	13
613	8
636	6, 7
684	1
704	7
705	6
740	1, 3, 4, 5, 6, 8, 10, 11, 12, 14
741	2, 6, 7, 8
766	12
818	7, 15
839	12

INDEX TO GLENCOE BIOLOGY: THE DYNAMICS OF LIFE

MYA: million years ago

Contents within parentheses are comments from the author, not concepts described in the textbooks.

Page	Evolutionary Concept	Article Reference
296–297	Mutations may have positive effects and play an important role in the evolution of a species. (The statement on evolution of species is not supported. Chapter 11 only relates to a small, information-losing change, not the rise of one kind from another.)	3:10, 3:13, 3:15, 3:22, 3:28
318	Sex chromosomes determine sex.	3:6, 6:7
366	Why It's Important section states evolution as a fact and says fossils and genetics are evidence.	3:24, 3:35, 4:4, 4:5
367	Timeline 2001: Hominid fossil discovered and dated at 6–7 million years old.	10:1, 10:3
367	Timeline 1778: The first time the idea of an earth older than a few thousand years is stated.	4:13, 4:14, 4:15
368	You will learn how rocks and fossils are correlated with the geologic timescale and biological events. You will also learn how molecules turn into cells as a foundation for understanding the evolutionary theory.	4:13, 4:14, 4:15
369	About 4.4 billion years ago earth might have cooled and led to millions of years of rainstorms. Some scientists propose life originated 3.9 billion years ago in earth's oceans.	5:1, 5:5
370	There is no direct evidence of early history. Oldest rocks date 3.9 billion years ago. (If there is no direct evidence and it cannot be observed and tested, can it be considered scientific?)	4:7
371	Figure 14.1 shows Ginkgo fossil and fresh leaf similarities.	4:7, 4:9
371	Fossils can be used to infer size, behavior, and diet.	3:30, 3:36
372	Figure 14.2 shows artificial layering of fossils from simple and older (*bottom*) to complex and younger (*top*), and the supporting text describes relative dating. (The time periods are not given, and no such layering exists, making it a misleading figure.)	4:12, 4:15
372	Relative dating assumes that rock layers all pile up in the same place or that the sequence can be directly correlated.	4:12, 4:15
372–375	Radiometric dating can provide dates for rocks. Scientists *know* the decay rates and scientists *always* use many methods to verify dates.	4:12, 4:15

Page	Evolutionary Concept	Article Reference
383	Complex organic molecules formed as amino acids and other molecules collected in heated pools.	5:1, 5:2, 5:5, 5:6
383	Protocell formation is presented as a precursor to cells—the second step needed to complete the evolution of molecules to cells. Simplified into two steps.	3:2, 5:5
383	Early atmosphere lacked oxygen. (Stated as fact, although p. 370 states that we cannot directly know the conditions of the earth's early atmosphere.)	5:3, 5:5
384	Photosynthetic bacteria evolved and produced oxygen that created the ozone layer.	5:3, 5:5
384–385	Endosymbiont Theory used to explain evolution of cells containing mitochondria and chloroplasts.	6:6
387	Lab activity on dating rocks uses pennies in a box as a model. (Does not include assumptions of the model.)	4:12, 4:15
388	After a discussion of the origin of life includes RNA world, chemical evolution, panspermia, and divine origins, the student is asked to weigh the evidence and decide. The web link connects only to evolutionary theories.	5:2, 5:4, 5:5, 5:6
389	The idea that small molecules can form complex organic molecules is given as fact without explaining the difficulties.	5:1, 5:2, 5:5, 5:6
390–391	Questions 5, 11, 13, 14, 15, 18, 19, 21, and 23 expect evolutionary ideas as answers.	
392	Students will analyze, compare, and contrast evolution and its processes.	1:3, 3:23, 3:24
392	Why It's Important section states that the evolution theory is key to understanding biology.	3:1, 3:7
392	Understanding the Photo section equates evolution with natural selection.	3:10, 3:11, 3:12, 3:13, 3:15, 3:16, 3:19, 3:22, 3:23, 3:27, 3:28, 3:35
393	The introductory paragraph implies evolution is necessary to understand biology and that the fossil evidence supports Darwin.	3:1, 3:7
393	An old earth is assumed by evidence from geologists.	3:13, 3:25, 3:29

Page	Evolutionary Concept	Article Reference
403	Text claims that all evidences are used together to determine relationships.	3:6, 3:7
404–411	Text discusses natural selection causing variation in populations. Every example is variation within one kind of animal, but it is used as support for evolution. (No explanation is given for how one kind can evolve into another.)	3:1, 3:5, 3:11, 3:12
411	Gradualism is supported by some fossil evidence but not consistent with the Cambrian explosion discussed on p. 377.	3:24, 3:29, 3:35, 4:13
411	Elephant speciation is supported by punctuated equilibrium hypothesis and fossils. Figure 15.17 shows elephant evolution sequence.	3:35
411	The fossil record supports gradualism (slow change) and punctuated equilibrium (rapid change).	3:24, 3:29, 3:35, 4:13
412	Natural selection leads to divergent evolution in a population.	3:10, 3:11, 3:12, 3:13, 3:15, 3:16, 3:19, 3:22, 3:23, 3:27, 3:28, 3:35
413	Convergent evolution is described for two desert plants and is evidence for evolution.	3:6, 3:7, 3:33
417	Study Guide repeats evolutionary ideas.	
418–419	Questions 8, 9, 11, 12, 13, 14, 15, 17, 21, 22, 23, and 24 all expect evolutionary ideas as answers.	
420	Chapter objectives indicate a common ancestor for all primates, with humans evolving from that ancestor.	3:6, 3:7, 10:1, 10:3
421	Humans are grouped with primates.	3:6, 3:7, 10:1, 10:3
423–424	Similarities in primates are evidence of evolutionary history.	3:6, 3:7, 10:1, 10:3
425	Common ancestor for humans based on structural and social similarities.	3:6, 3:7, 10:1, 10:3
426	Anthropoid fossils dated to 40 MYA and evolved into different groups of primates.	3:6, 3:7, 10:1, 10:3

Page	Evolutionary Concept	Article Reference
453	Most scientists see theropods as bird ancestors.	2:5, 3:24, 3:35, 4:17
454–455	Figure 17.8 shows a fan diagram of six kingdoms and earth's history.	3:6, 3:7, 3:8, 3:13, 3:19
456	Prokaryotes appear 3.4 billion years ago.	6:1, 6:2
458	Fungi appear 400 MYA.	3:6, 3:7, 6:3
458	Plants appear 400 MYA.	7:1, 7:3
459	Animals appear 600 MYA.	6:3
462	Molecular clocks are discussed as a tool to measure evolutionary time.	2:8, 3:6, 3:29
463	Study Guide repeats evolutionary ideas.	
464	Questions 3, 5, and 7 expect evolutionary ideas as answers.	
466–469	Review of geologic timescale, origin of life, and evolution.	
471	Questions 11, 12, 13, 14, 15, 17, and 18 expect evolutionary ideas as answers.	
484	Common ancestor for eubacteria and archaebacteria several billion years ago.	5:5, 6:4
490–491	Bacteria adapted to increasing concentration of oxygen in the atmosphere.	5:5, 6:5
498	Antibiotic resistance in bacteria is discussed but not linked to evolution. (Many teachers will use this as an example of evolution.)	3:13, 3:22, 3:28
508–509	Malaria is discussed but not linked to sickle-cell anemia. (The relationship between malaria and sickle-cell anemia is often used to support evolution.)	3:23, 3:28, 3:34
520–521	Origin of protists is discussed, including a fan diagram of ancestry.	3:7
543	Origin of fungi is discussed, including a fan diagram of ancestry.	3:6, 3:7
556	Timeline extends to 9,000 BC.	4:12, 4:13, 4:14
557	Timeline uses 10,000-year-old example of lupine seed germination.	4:12, 4:13, 4:14
559	Common ancestor of green algae and plants is discussed.	7:2, 7:3, 7:4

Page	Evolutionary Concept	Article Reference
824–825	All reptiles come from the stem reptile ancestors. Birds are the descendants of dinosaurs. Figure 31.11 shows fan diagram of reptile evolution. Birds are closely linked to dinosaurs in the fan diagram.	9:4
826	Figure 31.12 and text say most scientists agree birds came from theropod dinosaurs.	2:5, 3:35, 4:17
826	Feather is a modified protein scale.	2:5, 3:35, 9:9
827	Wings are modified limbs for flight.	2:5, 3:35
832–833	Origin of birds from theropods is discussed. Figure 31.18 shows fan diagram of bird evolution directly from a theropod.	2:5, 3:35, 4:17
837	Study Guide repeats evolutionary ideas.	
838	Questions 12 and 13 expect evolutionary ideas as answers.	
840	Objective is to compare modern mammals to their ancient ancestors. Includes humans as mammals.	9:7
841	Feathers and hair evolved from reptilian scales.	9:9
843	Text and Mini-lab 32.1 ask students to infer diet from teeth.	3:30, 3:36
844	Figure 32.3 explains teeth as adapted to diet.	3:30, 3:36
847	Humans are grouped with primates.	3:6, 3:7, 10:1, 10:3
849	Placental mammals evolved because of the advantage of internal development.	9:7
849	Plate tectonics is used to explain isolation of marsupials in Australia because they didn't compete with placental mammals that evolved elsewhere.	9:11
850–851	Origin of mammals is attributed to therapsids at 125 MYA. Figure 32.10 shows fan diagram of mammalian evolution from therapsids.	9:7
856	Question 12 uses evolution of hair.	9:9
862	Courtship has evolved through natural selection.	6:7, 9:13
882–883	Evolution of reptilian features is reiterated.	
1006	Amniotic egg evolution is mentioned.	9:4

INDEX TO PRENTICE HALL BIOLOGY (CAMPBELL)

MYA: million years ago

Contents within parentheses are comments from the author, not concepts described in the textbooks.

Page	Evolutionary Concept	Article Reference
54	Fixed action patterns are linked to an "ultimate cause." Hypothesis does not explain how it arose in the first place.	1:2, 1:3, 3:4
81–87	Properties of water and the anthropic principle are discussed.	3:2, 5:4
180	All cells come from preexisting cells.	5:1, 5:6, 6:1
193	Sex chromosomes determine sex.	3:6, 6:7
206	Mendel succeeded because he was a careful scientist.	3:10, 3:13, 3:15, 3:21
238–241	Proteins are assembled from DNA, which requires proteins to transcribe the DNA.	3:20
243	Mutations are the ultimate source of genetic diversity.	3:1, 3:10, 3:13, 3:15, 3:16, 3:19, 3:21, 3:22, 3:23, 3:28
249	DNA sequence and skull bones provide evidence of evolutionary relationships.	3:6, 3:7, 10:4, 10:5
250	Abnormal number of chromosomes usually leads to miscarriage in humans. (Also true for most animals.)	3:16
266	Bacteria can acquire new DNA through several mechanisms.	3:13, 3:22, 3:28
268	Plasmids convey resistance to antibiotics.	3:13, 3:22, 3:28
274–277	Genetic engineering is discussed.	3:37
285	Regulatory genes are given as a method for understanding evolutionary relationships.	3:7, 3:32
290	Introduction states evolution as a fact and suggests that a common ancestor is supported by the fossil record.	3:10, 3:11, 3:12, 3:13, 3:15, 3:16, 3:19, 3:22, 3:23, 3:27, 3:28, 3:35
290–291	Webquest to explore the bird/dinosaur fossil evidence.	2:5, 3:35, 4:17
292	Evolution is change in life over an immense time.	3:2, 3:7, 3:11, 3:13, 3:19, 3:24, 3:27, 3:28
292	In the 1700s many people believed the earth was less than 10,000 years old. Geologic time was accepted as a fact that removed young-earth ideas from acceptance in the 1700s.	4:13, 4:14, 4:15
295	Figure 14-5 states as fact that slow erosion caused Grand Canyon features.	4:10, 4:11

Page	Evolutionary Concept	Article Reference
295	Figure 14-6 says that fossils on mountains are evidence of major geologic change—assumes uniformitarian action in the text.	3:24, 3:29, 3:35, 4:13
295	Darwin used uniformitarian geology as a basis for evolutionary time in biology.	3:13, 3:25, 3:29
297	Natural selection acts as populations spread over millions of years.	3:13, 3:25, 3:29
297	Charles Darwin's theory was valuable because it connected many ideas together.	3:1, 3:3, 3:4, 3:7, 3:13, 3:24
298	Evolution can be defined as change over time or life's history on earth.	3:2, 3:7, 3:11, 3:13, 3:19, 3:24, 3:27, 3:28
299	Fossils and rock layers form over millions of years.	3:24, 4:1, 4:2, 4:3, 4:6, 4:8
299	Objectives: correlate homology, geographic distribution, and molecular similarities as evidence of evolution.	3:7
299	Evolution is identified as a historical science based on clues from all aspects of life.	1:1, 1:2, 3:1
299	Younger rocks are on top of the fossil record and provide a relative age.	4:12, 4:15
300	Chemical traces in 3.8 BYO rocks are signs of earliest life on earth.	4:7
300	The fossil record provides evidence of earth's changing life.	3:24, 3:29, 4:13, 4:14
300	Whales evolved from land animals over 40 MYA. Figure 14-11 shows fossil whale evidence.	3:9, 3:29
300	Prokaryotes were present at 3.5 billion years ago. A date which is supported by molecular evidence.	6:1, 6:2
300–301	Marsupials evolved in Australia due to isolation.	9:11
301	Homologous anatomy describes evolution. Figure 14-13 shows color-coded comparison of forelimbs.	3:6, 3:7, 3:33
302	Vestigial structures have no clear function and are often reduced in size. Whale pelvis, human skeleton, and goose bumps are described as vestigial in the text and Figure 14-14.	3:7, 3:8, 3:9, 3:24
302–303	Embryonic recapitulation is used as evidence of evolution. Figure 14-15 shows bird and human embryo comparison, including throat pouches, backbone, and tail.	3:7, 3:31

Page	Evolutionary Concept	Article Reference
303	DNA sequence provides evidence of evolutionary relationships.	3:6, 3:7, 10:4, 10:5
303	Molecular similarities allow scientists to form a testable hypothesis about evolutionary relationships. (Fails to mention the assumptions the hypothesis is based on and the historical nature of the hypothesis.)	1:1, 1:2, 3:1, 3:6, 3:7
303–304	Text and Figure 14-16 use hemoglobin similarities to prove a "testable" hypothesis that some animals are more closely related to humans than others. (Many assumptions involved, and many exceptions are excluded.)	3:6, 3:7
304	Online Activity discusses homologous structures.	3:6, 3:7, 3:33
304	DNA has passed from the first living organism to all other organisms.	3:6, 3:7
304	Chimps and humans have a 5% DNA difference.	3:6, 10:4, 10:5
305	Darwin's theory is the best explanation for evolution.	1:3, 3:23, 3:24
305	The finches on the Galapagos evolved from a single species.	3:1, 3:5, 3:6, 3:11, 3:12, 3:13, 3:28
307	Artificial selection is evidence for evolution. Figure 14-20 and text use dogs as an example.	1:3, 3:1, 3:13
307–308	Pesticide resistance in beetles is evidence for evolution. Discussed in text and Figure 14-21.	3:13, 3:28
310	Mendel succeeded because he was a careful scientist.	3:10, 3:13, 3:15, 3:21
310	Genetic variation/mutation is the raw material for evolution.	3:1, 3:10, 3:13, 3:15, 3:16, 3:19, 3:21, 3:22, 3:23, 3:28
311	Microevolution is defined the same way as molecules-to-man evolution.	3:1, 3:12, 3:13, 3:27
314	Genetic variation/mutation is the raw material for evolution.	3:1, 3:10, 3:13, 3:15, 3:16, 3:19, 3:21, 3:22, 3:23, 3:28
314	Natural selection rapidly increases the frequency of favorable mutations in bacteria.	3:10, 3:13, 3:15, 3:22, 3:28
316	Finch beaks change much faster than Darwin thought.	3:1, 3:5, 3:11, 3:12, 3:13, 3:27

Page	Evolutionary Concept	Article Reference
335	Fossil plants have been found in Idaho with chlorophyll in them. (This defies the idea of millions of years as the substances would surely have decomposed by now.)	4:6
335	Objectives: use geologic dates, fossil dating, and plate tectonics to understand evolution.	4:13, 4:14, 4:15, 4:20
335–336	Fossils can be read as history in layers. Fossil record displays macroevolution.	4:4, 4:5
336	Briefly mentions the composite nature of the geologic column.	3:24, 3:29, 4:13, 4:14
336	Cambrian explosion is briefly mentioned. (See p. 515 for more.)	3:24, 4:16
336–337	Teacher demonstration uses a line on a board to represent geologic time to show short human history, animal history, etc. Text uses an analogy of a year to earth's history. Geologic time is discussed in text and Figure 15-18.	4:12, 4:13, 4:14
336-339	Relative ages of fossils and rock layers can be determined by the positions of the layers. Absolute age must be found by radiometric dating.	4:12, 4:15
337	The geologic time scale shows an increase in complexity over billions of years.	3:24, 3:29, 4:13, 4:14
338	Absolute ages of rocks are found using radiometric dating. Half-life is unaffected by other conditions. Figure 15-19 shows relative/absolute dating of sedimentary layers. Different isotopes are used for different samples.	4:12, 4:15
339	Species diverged as the continents split 180 MYA.	9:11, 4:20
339	Pangaea was the only land 250 MYA, then it split at 180 MYA and caused divergent evolution in species. Figure 15-21 shows the long-age view of plate tectonics. The plates move at a uniform rate.	4:20
340	Internet Activities are on carbon dating and dinosaur evolution.	4:12, 4:15
340	Meteorite extinction theory describes mass extinction in text and Figure 15-22.	2:5, 4:18, 4:19
341	Linnaeus developed taxonomy.	2:1
341	Objectives: relate evolutionary and molecular biology with classification using cladograms.	2:2

Page	Evolutionary Concept	Article Reference
357	Early earth had a reducing atmosphere with little or no oxygen.	5:3, 5:5
357	Limitations of chirality and hydrolysis are not discussed with respect to formation of proteins in student text, but they are mentioned in teacher notes.	5:1, 5:2, 5:5, 5:6
358	RNA world hypothesis in text and Figure 16-3 suggests information can arise in early earth.	3:2, 5:2, 5:5
358	Precells form when lipids are included with organic molecules, explained in the text and also in Figure 16-4. (No explanation of where the lipids originated is provided.)	3:2, 5:5
359	Online activity on Miller's hypothesis.	5:3, 5:5, 5:6
359	Four stages of cell formation are given, but they cannot prove chemical evolution happened.	3:2, 5:1, 5:2, 5:3, 5:5, 5:6
359	Figure 16-5 and text suggest that life may have first formed in deep-sea vents.	3:2, 5:5, 5:6
361	The common ancestor for both domains of bacteria originated early in evolution.	5:5, 6:4
364	Prokaryotic cells generate genetic variability by exchanging DNA. Also shown in Figure 16-12.	3:13, 3:22, 3:28
366	Early earth had a reducing atmosphere with little or no oxygen.	5:3, 5:5
366	Organisms had to evolve as a result of the "oxygen revolution."	5:5, 6:5
366	Photosynthetic bacteria created the oxygen in earth's atmosphere.	5:3, 5:5
370	Mutations convey resistance to antibiotics in bacteria.	3:13, 3:22, 3:28
376–377	Questions 1, 7, 10, and 20 expect evolutionary ideas as answers.	
380–381	Evolutionary relationship of protists is too unsettled and complex for biology students; so protists are generally grouped based on common characteristics. DNA evidence explains evolutionary history.	3:6, 3:7
392	Over long periods of time, diatoms form thick layers.	3:24, 4:1, 4:2, 4:3, 4:6, 4:8
395	Fungi, plants, and animals evolved from protists hundreds of millions of years ago.	3:6, 3:7
395	Objective: describe endosymbiont hypothesis.	6:6

Page	Evolutionary Concept	Article Reference
395-397	Protists evolved from prokaryotes over 1 billion years ago. Fan diagram based on DNA of protists, plants, fungi, and animals in Figure 17-20.	3:6, 3:7, 6:6
395–397	Text and Figures 17-18, 19 show how mitochondria evolved before chloroplasts in primitive cells. Webquest on endosymbiosis.	6:6
398–399	Questions 7, 17, 23, and 25 expect evolutionary ideas as answers.	
411	Fungi evolved to live with plants and algae in symbiotic relationships.	3:6
418	Plants occur late in earth's history and colonized the land as algae evolved.	7:4
420	Plants evolved from an algal ancestor similar to charophytes shown in Figure 19-1.	7:2, 7:3, 7:4
420	First plant fossils dated at 475 MYA.	7:1, 7:3
420–422	Adaptations in seed development and dispersal, water retention, lignin for structure, and soil/air structures were necessary for plants to colonize land. Figures 19-2, 3 and 4 detail theses adaptations.	7:4
422–424	Four stages of plant evolution include emergence onto land, lignin and vascular structure, seed development, and flower development. Figure 19-5 shows cladogram of four points. Online activity explores plant cladogram.	7:4
425	Cladogram of bryophyte evolution.	7:4
427	Forests 359–299 MYA were dominated by ferns.	7:3
427	Cladogram of pteridophyte evolution and Figure 19-9 shows a Carboniferous forest. Figure 19-11 relates different species alive in the Carboniferous Period.	7:3
431–433	Gymnosperms evolved pollen, seeds, and smaller gametophytes. Cladogram shown for gymnosperms. Gymnosperms replaced pteridophytes in the Carboniferous swamps.	7:3, 7:4
434	Angiosperms evolved flowers with odors and protected seeds as relatively late evolutionary adaptations. Cladogram of angiosperm development shown.	7:3, 7:4

Page	Evolutionary Concept	Article Reference
555	Salamanders walk as early tetrapods may have, and caecilians evolved to lose their limbs.	9:2, 9:3
555	Amphibians exhibit evolutionary adaptations that allowed them to live on land.	9:2, 9:3
556–557	Questions 5, 6, 15, and 23 expect evolutionary ideas as answers.	
558	Amphibians began adaptation to life on land; and then reptiles, mammals, and birds evolved from them.	9:2, 9:3
558	Ancient reptiles are the ancestors of birds and mammals.	9:4
560–561	Amniotic egg, internal fertilization, and keratin in the skin are evolutionary adaptations of amniotes.	9:4
561	Keratin is found in scales, feather, and hair.	9:9
562	First fossil reptile dated at 300 MYA.	9:4
562	One group of dinosaurs may have been homeothermic and the ancestor to birds.	2:5, 3:35, 9:4
562	Dinosaurs may have become extinct due to a meteorite collision.	2:5, 4:18, 4:19
563	Turtles have changed little from fossils in the Mesozoic era.	4:9, 9:4, 9:5
563–564	Snakes and lizards are not as closely related to the dinosaurs as the crocodiles are to dinosaurs and birds.	2:5, 3:35, 9:4
564	Cladistics suggests crocodiles are more closely related to birds than to lizards and snakes.	2:5, 3:24, 3:35, 4:17
564	Snakes have many adaptations for catching prey.	9:8
564	Extensive fossil evidence points to crocodilians as the closest living relative to dinosaurs.	2:5, 3:35, 9:4
566	Evidence suggests birds are reptiles.	2:5, 3:24, 3:35, 4:17
566	Feathers are modified scales.	2:5, 3:35, 9:9
566	Birds have adapted to flight with feathers, wings, air sacs, 4-chambered heart, hollow bones, and endothermy.	2:5, 3:35, 9:9
566–567	Birds began as feathered reptiles. Fossils from China from 100 MYA show feathers on dinosaurs. Figure 26-10 shows *Archaeopteryx* as a modern bird ancestor.	2:5, 3:35
568–569	Adaptations in birds are assumed to be evolutionary in nature.	2:5, 3:35, 9:9

Page	Evolutionary Concept	Article Reference
577	*H. sapiens* originated in Africa from an unknown ancestor, which is confirmed with DNA evidence.	10:1, 10:3
577	Earliest *H. sapiens* fossil at 195,000 years ago.	10:1, 10:3
577	Online Activity focuses on human origins.	10:1, 10:3
577	Figure 26-23 shows three skulls that are evidence of evolution of humans.	10:1, 10:3
577	Neanderthals coexisted but did not evolve into humans.	10:1, 10:3, 10:6
580–581	Questions 2, 6, 7, 8, 10, 11, 16, 19, and 26 expect evolutionary ideas as answers.	

INDEX TO PRENTICE HALL BIOLOGY (MILLER)

Page	Evolutionary Concept	Article Reference
3	Myths about nature are discussed.	1:1, 1:2, 1:3
3–14	No distinction between operation and historical science.	1:1, 1:2, 3:1
5–6	Hypotheses must be testable. Science can't answer all questions.	1:1, 1:3
6	Scientific knowledge is always advancing our understanding.	1:1, 1:2, 3:1
10	A key assumption of science is that observations should be repeatable.	1:1, 1:2, 1:3
13–14	Pasteur showed that all living things come from other living things.	5:1, 5:6
14	Theories allow scientists to make predictions.	1:1, 1:2, 1:3
15	Marsupials evolved in Australia as plate tectonics split the continents millions of years ago.	9.11
16	Living things changing over time is used as a characteristic of life.	1:3, 3:1, 3:13
17	There are limits to the differences in offspring—flies produce flies, etc.	3:1, 3:10, 3:13, 3:15, 3:16, 3:19, 3:21, 3:22, 3:23, 3:28
20	The order of fossil deposits allows scientists to "know" that fish have evolved.	4:12, 4:15
20	Evolution is change in a group over time. Figure 1-20	1:3, 3:2, 3:4, 3:13, 3:23
36	Geologists use isotopes to determine the age of rocks and fossils.	4:12, 4:15
74	Dinosaurs lived millions of years ago.	9:6

MYA: million years ago

Contents within parentheses are comments from the author, not concepts described in the textbooks.

Page	Evolutionary Concept	Article Reference
125	Competition leads to the evolution of species.	1:3, 3:13, 3:23, 3:28, 3:35
129	Figure 5-10 shows graph of human population to 10,000 BC.	4:12, 4:13, 4:14
140	Figure 6-2, three Stone age people are discussed.	1:2, 10:1
140	Prehistoric people caused extinctions in North America 12,000 years ago.	1:2, 10:1
141	Humans began farming 11,000 years ago.	1:2, 10:1
141	The last ice age ended 11,000 years ago. (Contradicted on T434)	9:14
144	Fossil fuels formed over hundreds of millions of years.	7:3
170	New cells are produced from existing cells.	5:1, 5:6
171	Endosymbiont theory in a timeline of cell history.	6:6
173	Prokaryotes evolved before eukaryotes.	6:1, 6:2
180	Endosymbiont theory discussed. Chloroplasts and mitochondria evolved from prokaryotic symbiosis.	6:6
211	There was very little oxygen in the atmosphere 3.3 billion years ago until photosynthesis evolved.	5:3, 5:5
253	Stem cells are discussed and students are encouraged to discuss the moral issues involved.	
263–266	Text omits that Mendel was a creationist who rejected Darwin's ideas and showed static nature of inheritance	3:10, 3:13, 3:15, 3:21
291, 293	DNA contains information.	3:2, 5:2, 5:5
297	Histones have changed very little during evolution to protect DNA.	3:6, 3:15, 3:21
302	Introns and exons may have been important in evolution.	3:10, 3:13, 3:16
307–308	Most mutations are harmful or neutral. (Contradicted on T394.)	3:10, 3:13, 3:16
308	Beneficial mutations can help in new environments.	3:10, 3:13, 3:15, 3:22, 3:28
308	Mutations are the source of variability in a species.	3:1, 3:10, 3:13, 3:15, 3:16, 3:19, 3:21, 3:22, 3:23, 3:28

Page	Evolutionary Concept	Article Reference
378–379	Darwin published *On the Origin of Species* after waiting many years.	3:1, 3:3, 3:4, 3:13, 3:24
380	The struggle for existence can be compared to artificial selection and is central to Darwin's theory of evolution.	1:3, 3:1, 3:10, 3:11, 3:12, 3:13, 3:22, 3:23, 3:27
381	Natural selection cannot be seen directly, only in populations over many generations.	1:3, 3:1, 3:13
382	Fossils are a record of life on earth over millions of years, not thousands.	3:24, 3:29, 4:13, 4:14
382	All life on earth shares a common ancestor. Figure 15-13	3:6, 3:7, 3:8, 3:13, 3:19
383	Hundreds of transitional fossils have been found to support evolution.	3:24, 3:29, 3:35, 4:13
383	Convergent evolution happens in similar environments in different geographic areas.	3:6, 3:7, 3:33
383	Gaps in the fossil record do not weaken evolutionary theory; they just don't allow a full understanding of how some species evolved.	3:24, 3:29, 3:35, 4:13
384	Vestigial structures in humans include appendix, tailbone, and ear muscles. Vestigial structures do not serve important functions. Fig 15-16	3:7, 3:8
384	Homologous structures can be used to classify organisms.	3:6, 3:7, 3:29
384–385	Homologous structures develop from the same clumps of cells demonstrating common ancestry. Figure 15-15	3:6, 3:7, 3:33
385	Despite "fudged" drawings by Haeckel, the same groups of cells develop in the same order producing the homologous structures in vertebrates. Figure 15-17 shows similar embryos. The similarity of human and other vertebrate embryos is evidence of a common ancestor.	3:7, 3:31
386	Evolution is the "grand unifying theory of the life sciences" and is vital to medical science.	3:1, 3:7

Page	Evolutionary Concept	Article Reference
386	Natural selection causes evolution.	1:3, 3:1, 3:10, 3:11, 3:12, 3:13, 3:22, 3:23, 3:27
386	Biology, geology, and physics confirm Darwin's ideas of evolution.	3:7
386	There is uncertainty about how life began.	3:2, 5:1, 5:2, 5:3, 5:5, 5:6
387	Lucy dated 3.2 million years old and Australopithecines evolved 4 MYA to walk upright before large brains evolved. Laetoli footprints confirm this.	10:1, 10:3
389–390	Questions 7, 9, 10, 11, 13, 14, 16, 20, 21, 22, 23, 24, 25, 26, 27, 28, 31, 33, 34, and 35 expect evolutionary ideas as answers.	
391	Questions 4, 5, 7, and 8 expect evolutionary ideas as answers.	
392	Mutations are the source of variability in a species.	3:1, 3:10, 3:13, 3:15, 3:16, 3:19, 3:21, 3:22, 3:23, 3:28
393	Text omits that Mendel was a creationist who rejected Darwin's ideas and showed static nature of inheritance	3:10, 3:13, 3:15, 3:21
393	Evolution is described in genetic terms. DNA models and identifying genes have increased the understanding of evolution.	3:10, 3:11, 3:12, 3:13, 3:15, 3:16, 3:19, 3:22, 3:23, 3:27, 3:28, 3:35
394	Gene pools are important in evolutionary theory as populations change over time.	1:3, 3:13, 3:23, 3:28, 3:35
394–395	Mutations are the source of variability in a species.	3:1, 3:10, 3:13, 3:15, 3:16, 3:19, 3:21, 3:22, 3:23, 3:28
394, 397	Evolution is the change in gene frequency in a population.	1:3, 3:13, 3:23, 3:28, 3:35
397	Natural selection only affects individuals not genes, and only populations can evolve.	1:3, 3:1, 3:10, 3:11, 3:12, 3:13, 3:22, 3:23, 3:27

Page	Evolutionary Concept	Article Reference
398	Environmental pressures cause populations to evolve.	1:3, 3:1, 3:10, 3:11, 3:12, 3:13, 3:22, 3:23, 3:27
400	Genetic drift causes evolution.	3:5, 3:10, 3:11, 3:12, 3:13, 3:15, 3:22
400	Fruit flies and beetles evolve through genetic drift. Figure 16-9	3:5, 3:10, 3:11, 3:12, 3:13, 3:15, 3:22
401	Evolution stops with genetic equilibrium.	3:10, 3:11, 3:12, 3:13, 3:15, 3:16, 3:19, 3:22, 3:23, 3:27, 3:28, 3:35
403	Antibiotic resistance is an example of evolution in action.	3:13, 3:22, 3:28
404–405	New species evolve as populations are separated from one another. Figure 16-2 Kaibab squirrels evolved apart from Albert squirrels.	3:5, 3:10, 3:11, 3:12, 3:13, 3:15, 3:22
406–409	Variation in finch beaks over time is evidence of evolution. Figure 16-13, 14	3:1, 3:10, 3:13, 3:15, 3:16, 3:19, 3:21, 3:22, 3:23, 3:28
406–409	Galapagos species evolved from ancestral South American species.	3:5, 3:10, 3:11, 3:12, 3:13, 3:15, 3:22
410	All life on earth shares a common ancestor. Figure 15-13	3:6, 3:7, 3:8, 3:13, 3:19
410	Fossils show that life evolved over 3 billion years and as more fossils are found evolution will be supported.	3:24, 3:29, 3:35, 4:7, 4:13
410	Antibiotic resistance is an example of evolution in action.	3:13, 3:22, 3:28
410	Evolution unites all of biology and makes useful predictions.	3:1, 3:7
410	Evolution is a well-tested explanation of a broad set of scientific evidences.	1:2, 1:3, 3:4
413–414	Questions 10, 16, 22, 23, 24, 30, and 33 expect evolutionary ideas as answers.	

Page	Evolutionary Concept	Article Reference
425	The leap from nonlife to life is the greatest gap in scientific hypotheses of earth history.	3:2, 5:1, 5:2, 5:3, 5:5, 5:6
425	Proteinoid microspheres might have acquired the characteristics of living cells. Figure 17-9	3:2, 5:5
425	Scientists cannot understand how DNA and RNA evolved the complex information and duplication systems.	3:2, 5:2, 5:5
425	RNA could have been the first genetic molecule and may have given rise to DNA and protein systems.	3:2, 5:2, 5:5
426	Oxygen began to accumulate after photosynthesis evolved 2.2 billion years ago. Figure 17-11	5:3, 5:5
426	Organisms evolved to use oxygen and protect themselves from it as it accumulated in the atmosphere.	5:5, 6:5
426	The first life evolved in the absence of oxygen about 3.5 billion years ago.	5:3, 5:5
427	Organisms evolved internal membranes 2.2 billion years ago.	6:1
427	Chloroplasts and mitochondria evolved through an endosymbiotic relationship. Several evidences support this conclusion. Figure 17-12	6:6
428	Multicellular life was able to evolve more rapidly as a result of sexual reproduction.	3:6, 6:7
428	Sexual reproduction evolved and accelerated evolution.	3:6, 6:7
429	The fossil record is missing many pieces but scientists have good evolutionary histories of many groups.	3:6, 3:7, 5:6, 8:1
429	Multicellular life evolved to its present day diversity.	5:6, 8:2
429	During the Precambrian life evolved from simple anaerobes to eukaryotes but few fossils were left behind.	5:6, 8:3
429	Life had evolved to great diversity by the beginning of the Cambrian period though it is not clear how. Figure 17-14	4:16
430	Most animal phyla evolved in the "Cambrian Explosion".	3:24, 4:16
430	Some arthropods became the first animals to live on land during the Ordovician Period.	3:13

Page	Evolutionary Concept	Article Reference
458	Domains are based on how long they have been evolving independently.	2:3, 2:4
460–461	Figure 18-13 shows a tree of life with a ? as the original ancestor.	3:6, 3:7, 3:8, 3:13, 3:19
464–466	Questions 6, 7, 12, 15, 16, 17, 18, 19, 20, 21, 27, 32, 33, and 34 expect evolutionary ideas as answers.	
467	Questions 2, 5, and 8 expect evolutionary ideas as answers.	
472	Archaebacteria may be the ancestors of eukaryotes.	5:5, 6:4
483	Viruses evolved after the first cells and have been evolving since.	3:38
487	Bacteria evolve resistance as antibacterial compounds are used.	3:13, 3:22, 3:28
498	Different groups of protists likely evolved independently from archaebacteria.	6:3
498	Protists were the first eukaryotes to evolve 1.5 billion years ago from the symbiosis of many cells. Figure 20-2	3:6, 3:7
498	Common classification of protists does not reflect evolutionary relationships.	3:6, 3:7
500	The Cliffs of Dover were raised up by geologic processes.	3:24, 4:1, 4:2, 4:3, 4:6, 4:8
506	Algae evolved different forms of chlorophyll as adaptations to ocean life.	3:7
511	Plants likely evolved from an algalike ancestor millions of years ago.	7:2, 7:3, 7:4
536	Penicillium likely evolved from an ascomycete.	3:6, 3:7
537	Fungi evolved along with the first land plants 460 MYA. Figure 21-11	3:6
541	Mycorrhizal associations were a critical adaptation in the evolution of land plants.	3:6
542	Plants and fungi are evolving together in partnership.	3:14
545–546	Questions 21, 25, 30, and 32 expect evolutionary ideas as answers.	
551	Oldest fossil plants at 470 MYA.	7:1, 7:3

INDEX TO HOLT BIOLOGY

MYA: million years ago

Contents within parentheses are comments from the author, not concepts described in the textbooks.

Page	Evolutionary Concept	Article Reference
156	Question 13 expects an evolutionary idea as an answer.	
162–169	Mendel succeeded because he was a careful scientist.	3:10, 3:13, 3:15, 3:21
180	Mutations are rare and can have negative effects.	3:10, 3:13, 3:16
180	Sickle-cell anemia is an example of a helpful mutation against malaria.	3:23, 3:28, 3:34
208–210	Proteins are used to translate DNA into proteins, and those proteins need to be transcribed and translated from the DNA.	3:20
216	Transposons could be a powerful mechanism in evolution and could explain how larger organisms developed from single cells.	3:10, 3:13, 3:16
219	Mutations usually disrupt protein function. Major types of mutations are shown.	3:10, 3:13, 3:16
220	DNA sequence can reveal evolutionary relationships.	2:8, 3:6, 3:7, 10:1, 10:3
228–243	Genetic engineering of plants and animals is discussed, including human applications.	3:37
232	Evolution of a gene can be studied by comparing nucleotide sequences.	2:8, 3:6, 3:7, 10:1, 10:3
252	4.5 billion years ago earth was a molten ball that cooled, oceans formed, and life evolved over hundreds of millions of years. This is supported by radiometric dating.	4:7
252	Objectives: understand radiometric dating, two models of origin of life, cell organization, and development of heredity.	4:13, 4:14, 4:15
252	Radiometric dating is discussed as an absolute process. (No mention of assumptions or faulty dating results.)	4:12, 4:15
253	Lab Activity on dating rocks using corn in a box as a model. (Does not include assumptions of the model.)	4:12, 4:15
253	It is a testable hypothesis that organic molecules necessary for life can form from nonliving matter.	3:2, 5:1, 5:2, 5:3, 5:5, 5:6
254	No oxygen or ozone layer was present on early earth. Reducing atmosphere is discussed and then rejected.	5:3, 5:5
254	Life may be present on Mars and other planets with oxygen and water.	3:2, 5:4

Page	Evolutionary Concept	Article Reference
262	Cambrian explosion has most life forms appearing and going through great evolutionary changes in a short period of geologic time.	3:24, 4:16
263	Five major extinction events occurred at 440, 360, 245, 65, and 35 MYA.	2:5, 4:18, 4:19
264	2.5 billion years ago cyanobacteria started producing oxygen.	5:3, 5:5
265	Plants likely evolved from photosynthetic protists.	7:2, 7:3, 7:4
265	First plant/fungus colonized land 430 MYA. Figure 12-12 shows fossil and living example. First plants to invade land probably had fungal symbionts because of the lack of organic matter in soil.	7:1, 7:3
266	Carboniferous forests formed coal beds and oil reservoirs over millions of years. Figure 12-14 shows forest.	7:3
266	Arthropods were the first land animals about 430 MYA.	3:13
267	First jawed fish dated at 430 MYA. Jaws provided an evolutionary advantage.	3:6, 9:2
267	Amphibians evolved 370 MYA as fish fins evolved into limbs. Figure 32-8 shows limb homology in fish and an early amphibian.	9:2, 9:3
267	First vertebrates were jawless fish at 530 MYA.	9:1
268	Continental drift over geologic time was important in evolution.	4:20
268	Therapsids gave rise to mammals in the Triassic.	9:7
268	Reptiles evolved from amphibians at 340 MYA as watertight skin and eggs evolved.	9:4
268	Birds evolved from feathered dinosaurs in the Jurassic.	2:5, 3:35, 4:17
268	Marsupials evolved in Australia and South America due to continents being once connected.	9:11
270–271	Questions 2, 3, 4, 5, 6, 9, 10, 11, 12, 13, and 15 expect evolutionary ideas as answers.	
271	Questions 1, 3, 4, 5, and 6 expect evolutionary ideas as answers.	
272–273	Lab activity to construct a timeline of earth's history.	4:13, 4:14, 4:15

Page	Evolutionary Concept	Article Reference
276	Most scientists agree evolution produced diversity seen today.	3:1, 3:7
277	Darwin found evidence for gradual change, supported by Lyell.	3:1, 3:7
277	People had previously believed in creation.	4:13, 4:14, 4:15
277–280	Darwin's book synthesized ideas from many people.	3:1, 3:3, 3:4, 3:13, 3:24
279	Definitions of adaptation, evolution, and natural selection are given in general terms and somewhat interchangeable.	1:3, 3:1, 3:13
281	Mutation and the recombination of alleles is an endless source of information for natural selection to act on.	1:3, 3:1, 3:10, 3:11, 3:12, 3:13, 3:22, 3:23, 3:27
281	Reproductive isolation is equated with evolution in squirrels.	3:1, 3:5, 3:6, 3:11, 3:12, 3:13, 3:28
282	Gradualism is contrasted with punctuated equilibrium. Drastic environmental changes may cause rapid evolution events.	3:24, 3:29, 3:35, 4:13
283	Evolution is almost universally accepted by scientists as the best explanation for diversity.	3:1, 3:7
283	Fossils are the most direct evidence of evolution.	3:24, 3:35, 4:4, 4:5
283	Fossils above are different from and younger than fossils in lower layers. Figure 13-7 supports this claim.	3:24, 3:35, 4:4, 4:5
283	Three points of evolution: 4.5-billion-year-old earth, organisms for most of history, common ancestor for all living organisms.	3:6, 3:7, 3:8, 3:13, 3:19, 4:7
283	Objectives: correlating fossils, molecular development, and homologies support evolution.	3:6, 3:24, 3:29
284–285	An accurate description of fossil formation is given, including rapid deposition of sediment.	4:6
284–285	Whales evolved from cow-like mammals that returned to the sea 60 MYA. Whale evolution from three fossil species is presented in Figure 13-8.	3:9, 3:29
285	Fossils are dated by the age of the rocks near the fossil. Fossils are put in order based on their age, as in Figure 13-8.	4:12, 4:15
286	Whale pelvis is vestigial.	3:7, 3:8, 3:9, 3:24

Page	Evolutionary Concept	Article Reference
286	Most scientists believe evolutionary history is present in development of embryos.	3:7, 3:31
286	Homologous structures had the same function in a common ancestor. Evidence of evolution shown in Figure 13-9.	3:6, 3:7, 3:33
286	All vertebrates have a tail, limb buds, and pharyngeal pouches at some point in their development.	3:7, 3:31
286	Vestigial structures are smaller or less functional, or they perform a different function from ancestral homologous structure.	3:7, 3:8
287	DNA evidence and comparative anatomy between living and fossil organisms confirm that evolution happened in the sequence seen in the fossil record.	3:6, 3:7
287	The more similar the amino acid sequence of two organisms, the more recently they shared a common ancestor. Figure 13-10 shows hemoglobin sequence comparison.	3:6, 3:7
288–291	Definitions of adaptation, evolution, and natural selection are given in general terms and are somewhat interchangeable.	1:3, 3:1, 3:13
289	Tuberculosis evolved resistance to antibiotics by a point mutation. Natural selection leads to evolution.	3:13, 3:22, 3:28
290	Changes in the beaks of Darwin's finches show how natural selection influences evolution. Beak shape is shown to change rapidly in Figure 13-13 and then return to normal condition. (There is no net change in the graph, so evolution has not occurred.)	3:1, 3:5, 3:11, 3:12, 3:13, 3:27
291	Natural selection results in evolution when a trait makes a species more fit.	3:10, 3:13, 3:15, 3:22, 3:28
292	New species have evolved as mutations have accumulated.	3:1, 3:5, 3:6, 3:11, 3:12, 3:13, 3:28
294	Questions 1, 2, 3, 5, 6, 8, 10, 11, 12, 13, 14, and 15 expect evolutionary ideas as answers.	
295	Questions 2, 5, 6, and 7 expect evolutionary ideas as answers.	
300	Linnaeus develops taxonomy.	2:1
305	Objectives: analogous structures are produced in convergent evolution, and cladograms are used to determine evolutionary relationships.	3:6, 3:7, 3:29

Page	Evolutionary Concept	Article Reference
362–364	Symbiotic organisms coevolved.	3:7, 3:14
380	Question 1 expects an evolutionary idea as an answer.	
392	We are currently in the biggest extinction event since 65 MYA.	2:5, 4:18, 4:19
413	The bacteria domain is older than Archaea domain. Figure 19-2 shows evolutionary tree of the three domains of life.	5:5, 6:4
413	Figure 19-2 shows phylogenetic tree of all life on earth inferred from rRNA sequence.	2:8, 3:6, 3:7, 3:8, 3:13, 3:19
414	Evolutionary relationships of bacteria are inferred from rRNA sequence and other enzymes.	5:5, 6:4
416	Genetic recombination is the raw material for evolution.	1:3, 3:1, 3:10, 3:11, 3:12, 3:13, 3:22, 3:23, 3:27
416	Multicellular organization was an important evolutionary milestone.	6:3
422	Plants evolved on land.	7:2, 7:3, 7:4
444	Cyanobacteria made earth's oxygen atmosphere.	5:3, 5:5
447	Bacteria evolved means of getting resources from humans.	3:7, 3:14
449	Mutations confer a resistance to antibiotics.	3:13, 3:22, 3:28
452	Questions 8 and 11 expect evolutionary ideas as answers.	
460	Animals, plants, and fungi evolved from protists.	3:6, 3:7
460	Protists evolved 1.5 billion years ago by endosymbiosis.	3:7
461	Multicellular organisms evolved in independent instances.	6:3
461	Cilia and flagella evolved in protists.	6:3
461	Common classification of protists does not reflect evolutionary relationships.	3:6, 3:7
461	Sexual reproduction and multicellularity first evolved in protists.	3:6, 6:3, 6:7
476	Question 1 expects an evolutionary idea as an answer.	
482	Fungi appeared 430 MYA and evolved from unicellular eukaryotes.	3:7
490	First plants to invade land probably had fungal symbionts because of the lack of organic matter in soil.	7:1, 7:3
499	Corn was grown 10,000 years ago.	4:12, 4:13, 4:14

Page	Evolutionary Concept	Article Reference
724	Meteorite landed in Yucatan 65 MYA and caused dinosaur extinction.	2:5, 4:18, 4:19
725	*Archaeopteryx* shares characteristics with birds and dinosaurs. Recent fossils in China, one shown in Figure 32-17, suggest birds evolved from dinosaurs.	2:5, 3:24, 3:35, 4:17
726	Bird evolution is based on limited fossil evidence and DNA analysis.	2:5, 3:24, 3:35, 4:17
726	The penguin's wings were modified by evolution.	2:5, 3:35
727	Most agree birds evolved from dinosaurs. Crocodiles and birds are more closely related to dinosaurs and each other than to other living reptiles.	2:5, 3:35, 4:17
727	Turtles have changed very little in structure over 200 million years.	4:9, 9:4, 9:5
727	Birds are closely related to crocodiles, and this may account for similarities. Many biologists think birds are descended from dinosaurs.	2:5, 3:35, 4:17
728	Therapsids gave rise to mammals in the Triassic.	9:7
728	First mammals appeared 220 MYA as dinosaurs evolved from thecodonts.	9:7
728	Mammals were small, insectivorous, and nocturnal during the age of the dinosaurs. Mammals diversified to replace dinosaurs after they became extinct.	9:7
728–729	Ice Age from 2 million to 10,000 years ago had huge mammals evolving.	9:14
730	Monotremes were the first mammals to evolve and to lay eggs.	9:12
731	Fossils suggest that the common ancestor of primates were small insectivorous mammals present 80 MYA.	3:6, 3:7, 9:10, 10:1, 10:3
731	First primates evolved 50 MYA.	3:6, 3:7, 10:1, 10:3
731	Modern primates evolved from prosimians common 38 MYA.	3:6, 3:7, 10:1, 10:3
731	Objective: identify evolutionary relationship between humans and apes, and the evidence of human ancestry.	3:6, 3:7, 10:1, 10:3
732	Diurnal primates evolved to exploit daytime niches.	3:6, 3:7, 10:1, 10:3

Page	Evolutionary Concept	Article Reference
732	Apes evolved 30 MYA.	3:6, 3:7, 10:1, 10:3
732	Humans grouped with apes in Figure 32-24.	3:6, 3:7, 10:1, 10:3
732	Chimps may have 5% difference in DNA. 287 amino acids are identical in the hemoglobin of humans and chimps.	3:6, 10:4, 10:5
732	Gorillas diverged 7 MYA and chimps diverged 4 MYA from a common ancestor, as shown in Figure 32-24.	3:6, 3:7, 10:1, 10:3
733	Earliest hominids date 5–7 MYA.	3:6, 3:7, 10:1, 10:3
733	Table 32-1 shows skeletal comparison of a gorilla and an australopithecine. Lucy skeleton is shown in Figure 32-25.	10:1, 10:3
733	Lucy dated at 3 MYA, and fossils show australopithecines walked upright. Skeleton shown in Figure 32-25.	10:1, 10:3
734	Fossils indicate a common ancestor for hominids and humans, but it is not clear how they are related.	3:6, 3:7, 10:1, 10:3
734	Evolutionary relationships are unclear based on fossils. Figure 32-26 shows timeline of fossils with no evolutionary relationships other than color coding.	3:6, 3:7, 10:1, 10:3
735	Objective: describe the evidence that *Homo sapiens* evolved in Africa.	10:1, 10:3
735	Chimps and apes can learn sign language better than vocal communication.	3:6, 10:4, 10:5
735	*H. habilis* in Africa used tools more than 2 MYA.	10:1, 10:3
736	*H. erectus* (Java man) evolved in Africa 1.5 MYA and migrated to Asia and Europe. This is probably a direct ancestor of *H. sapiens*.	10:1, 10:3
737	DNA sequence can reveal evolutionary relationships. Evolution of a group can be studied by comparing nucleotide sequences. mtDNA and ycDNA are discussed to show that humans evolved in Africa about 170,000 years ago.	2:8, 3:6, 3:7, 10:1, 10:3
737	Cave painting in Figure 32-30 is dated at 20,000 years.	10:1, 10:3
738	Modern humans evolved in Africa.	10:1, 10:3
738	Neanderthals in Europe and Asia evolved 130,000 years ago and were replaced as modern *H. sapiens* migrated from Africa.	10:1, 10:3, 10:6

Chapter 1: What Is Science?

Article # Reference

1:1 Duane Gish, "The Nature of Science and of Theories On Origins," Institute for Creation Research, http://www.icr.org/article/391.

1:2 Bodie Hodge, "Feedback: A "More Glorious" Means for Creation?" Answers in Genesis, http://www.answersingenesis.org/go/glorious.

1:3 Ken Ham, "Creation: Where's the Proof?" Answers in Genesis, http://www.answersingenesis.org/go/proof.

Chapter 2: Classifying Life

Article # Reference

2:1 Henry Morris, *Men of Science, Men of God* (Green Forest, Arkansas: Master Books, 1998), pp. 27–28.

2:2 John Ashton, ed., *In Six Days*, (Green Forest, Arkansas: Master Books, 2000) pp. 241–245, http://www.answersingenesis.org/home/Area/isd/jones.asp.

2:3 Paula Weston, "How To Read an Evolutionary Family Tree," http://www.answersingenesis.org/creation/v18/i3/familytree.asp.

2:4 Answers in Genesis, "Dinosaurs: Phylogenetic Chart," http://www.answersingenesis.org/go/phylogenetic-chart.

2:5 Steve Austin, "Archaeoraptor: Feathered Dinosaur from *National Geographic* Doesn't Fly," Institute for Creation Research, http://www.icr.org/article/464.

2:6 Ashby Camp, "On the Alleged Dinosaurian Ancestry of Birds," http://www.trueorigin.org/birdevo.asp.

2:7 Mike Matthews, "*Scientific American* Admits Creationists Hit a Sore Spot," Answers in Genesis, http://www.answersingenesis.org/go/sciam-sore.

2:8 Brad Harrub and Bert Thompson, "The Demise of Mitochondrial Eve," http://www.trueorigin.org/mitochondrialeve01.asp.

Chapter 3: Natural Selection vs. Evolution

Article # **Reference**

3:1   Ken Ham, ed., *The New Answers Book* (Green Forest, Arkansas: Master Books, 2006), pp. 271–282.

3:2   Bert Thompson, "Is Evolution a "Fact" of Science?" Apologetics Press, http://www.apologeticspress.org/modules.php?name=Read&cat=4&itemid=1985.

3:3   Tommy Mitchell, "Why Would an Evolutionist Become a Doctor?" Answers in Genesis, http://www.answersingenesis.org/articles/2008/07/21/why-would-evolutionist-become-doctor.

3:4   Gary Parker, *Creation Facts of Life: How Real Science Reveals the Hand of God* (Green Forest, Arkansas: Master Books, 2006), pp. 75–76, http://www.answersingenesis.org/cec/docs/cfl-pdfs.asp.

3:5   Ken Ham, "Did God Create Poodles?" Answers in Genesis, http://www.answersingenesis.org/go/poodles.

3:6   Gary Parker, *Creation Facts of Life: How Real Science Reveals the Hand of God* (Green Forest, Arkansas: Master Books, 2006), pp. 43–53, http://www.answersingenesis.org/cec/docs/cfl-pdfs.asp.

3:7   Jerry Bergman, "Does Homology Provide Evidence of Evolutionary Naturalism?" Answers in Genesis, http://www.answersingenesis.org/tj/v15/i1/homology.asp.

3:8   Richard Wilkinson, "Cutting Out a Useless Vestigial Argument,"Answers in Genesis, http://www.answersingenesis.org/creation/v26/i3/vestigial.asp.

3:9   Duane Gish, "When Is a Whale a Whale?" Institute for Creation Research, http://www.icr.org/article/379.

3:10   Ken Ham, ed., *The New Answers Book 2* (Green Forest, Arkansas: Master Books, 2008), pp. 25–34.

3:11   John Morris, "Does the Beak of the Finch Prove Darwin Was Wrong?" Institute for Creation Research, http://www.icr.org/article/1135.

3:12   Kenneth B. Cumming, "Reticulate Evolution," Institute for Creation Research, http://www.icr.org/article/418.

3:13   Gary Parker, *Creation Facts of Life: How Real Science Reveals the Hand of God* (Green Forest, Arkansas: Master Books, 2006), pp. 80–84, http://www.answersingenesis.org/cec/docs/cfl-pdfs.asp.

3:14   John Ashton, ed., *In Six Days*, (Green Forest, Arkansas: Master Books, 2000) pp. 61–74, http://www.answersingenesis.org/home/Area/isd/jones.asp.

3:15   Kenneth Patman, "Genetics: No Friend of Evolution," Answers in Genesis, http://www.answersingenesis.org/creation/v20/i2/genetics.asp.

Article #   **Reference**

3:16   Alexander Williams, "Copying Confusion," Answers in Genesis, http://www.answersingenesis.org/creation/v25/i4/DNAduplication.asp.

3:17   John Rendle-Short, "Man: The Image of God," Answers in Genesis, http://www.answersingenesis.org/creation/v4/i1/man.asp.

3:18   Answers in Genesis, "Evolution = Atheism," http://www.answersingenesis.org/home/area/tools/Quotes/provine.asp.

3:19   Gary Parker, *Creation Facts of Life: How Real Science Reveals the Hand of God* (Green Forest, Arkansas: Master Books, 2006), pp. 76–80, http://www.answersingenesis.org/cec/docs/cfl-pdfs.asp.

3:20   "Learning the Right Tricks about Life's Origin," *Creation* **13**(4):35, 1991, http://www.answersingenesis.org/creation/v13/i4/tricks.asp.

3:21   David DeWitt, "Startling Plant Discovery Presents Problems for Evolution," http://www.answersingenesis.org/docs2005/0406mutation_fixing.asp.

3:22   Kevin Anderson, "Is Bacterial Resistance to Antibiotics an Appropriate Example of Evolutionary Change?" *Creation Research Society Quarterly* **41**(4):318–326, 2005, http://www.trueorigin.org/bacteria01.asp.

3:23   David Demick, "Can Genetic Mutations Produce Positive Changes in Living Creatures?" http://www.christiananswers.net/q-eden/genetic-mutations.html.

3:24   Mark Van Bebber and Paul Taylor, "What Does the Fossil Record Teach Us about Evolution?" http://www.christiananswers.net/q-eden/edn-c006.html.

3:25   Russell Humphreys, "Evidence for a Young World," http://www.icr.org/article/1842.

3:26   Gallup Poll on Creationism, Aug 5–7, 2005, poll.gallup.com/content/default.aspx?ci=18748.

3:27   Gary Parker, *Creation Facts of Life: How Real Science Reveals the Hand of God,* Master Books, Green Forest, AR, pp. 84–108, 2006, http://www.answersingenesis.org/cec/docs/cfl-pdfs.asp.

3:28   Gary Parker, *Creation Facts of Life: How Real Science Reveals the Hand of God* (Green Forest, Arkansas: Master Books, 2006), pp. 108–125, http://www.answersingenesis.org/cec/docs/cfl-pdfs.asp.

3:29   Frank Sherwin, "Scientific Roadblocks To Whale Evolution," Institute for Creation Research, http://www.icr.org/article/433.

3:30   Paula Weston, "Camels—Confirmation of Creation," Answers in Genesis, http://www.answersingenesis.org/creation/v19/i4/camels.asp.

3:31   Tommy Mitchell and Elizabeth Mitchell, "Something Fishy about gill Slits!" Answers in Genesis, http://www.answersingenesis.org/articles/2007/03/14/fishy-gill-slits.

Article #   Reference

3:32   David DeWitt, "Hox Hype," Answers in Genesis, http://www.answersingenesis.org/docs2002/0215hox_hype.asp.

3:33   Frank Sherwin, "Living Light," Answers in Genesis, http://www.icr.org/article/231.

3:34   Answers in Genesis, "Sickle-cell Anemia Does Not Prove Evolution," http://www.answersingenesis.org/go/sickle-cell.

3:35   Gary Parker, *Creation Facts of Life: How Real Science Reveals the Hand of God* (Green Forest, Arkansas: Master Books, 2006), pp. 166–174, http://www.answersingenesis.org/cec/docs/cfl-pdfs.asp.

3:36   Bodie Hodge, "Unexpectedly Vegetarian Animals—What Does it Mean?" Answers in Genesis, http://www.answersingenesis.org/articles/2009/06/02/vegetarian-animals.

3:37   Georgia Purdom, "Virus 'Evolution' Benefits Mankind?" ANswers in Genesis, http://www.answersingenesis.org/docs2006/0222virus.asp.

3:38   Ryan Kitner, "Genetic Variance of Influenza Type A Avian Virus and Its Evolutionary Implications," Answers in Genesis, http://www.answersingenesis.org/go/bird-flu-evolving.

Chapter 4: Unlocking the Geologic Column

Article #   Reference

4:1   Answers in Genesis, "The Clock in the Rock," http://www.answersingenesis.org/creation/v19/i3/clock.asp.

4:2   Answers in Genesis, "Fascinating Fossil Fence-wire," http://www.answersingenesis.org/creation/v20/i3/fossil.asp.

4:3   Andrew Snelling, "Can Flood Geology Explain Thick Chalk Beds?" Answers in Genesis, http://www.answersingenesis.org/tj/v8/i1/chalk.asp.

4:4   "Fossils—Do They Get More Complex?" Answers in Genesis, http://www.answersingenesis.org/creation/v20/i2/fossils.asp.

4:5   Ken Ham, "The Fossils Say What?" Answers in Genesis, http://www.answersingenesis.org/creation/v4/i4/fossils.asp.

4:6   John Morris, "Dinosaur Soft Parts," Institute for Creation Research, http://www.icr.org/article/2032.

4:7   Answers in Genesis, "Ancient Organisms Stay the Same," http://www.answersingenesis.org/creation/v21/i3/news.asp.

4:8   Answers in Genesis, "Rocks Forming in Months," http://www.answersingenesis.org/creation/v17/i2/focus.asp.

Article # Reference

4:9   Answers in Genesis, "Rodent Resurrected?" http://www.answersingenesis.org/ articles/am/v1/n1/rodent-resurrected#fnList_1_2.

4:10   Andrew Snelling, "Rock Layers Folded, Not Fractured," Answers in Genesis, http:// www.answersingenesis.org/articles/am/v4/n2/folded-not-fractured.

4:11   John Morris, "A Canyon in Six Days!" Answers in Genesis, http://www. answersingenesis.org/go/walla-canyon.

4:12   John Woodmorappe, "*National Geographic* Plays the Dating Game," Answers in Genesis, http://www.answersingenesis.org/tj/v16/i1/dating_game.asp.

4:13   Mike Oard, "How Well Do Paleontologists Know Fossil Distribution?" Answers in Genesis, http://www.answersingenesis.org/tj/v14/i1/fossils.asp.

4:14   Steven A. Austin, "Ten Misconceptions about the Geologic Column," Institute for Creation Research, http://www.icr.org/article/242/107.

4:15   Andrew Snelling, "Radioisotopes and the Age of the Earth," Answers in Genesis, http://www.answersingenesis.org/articles/aid/v2/n1/radioisotopes-earth.

4:16   John Morris, "What Grows on Evolution's Tree?" Institute for Creation Research, http://www.icr.org/article/577.

4:17   Answers in Genesis, "Claws on Wings," Answers in Genesis, http://www. answersingenesis.org/creation/v5/i2/claws.asp.

4:18   Emil Silvestru, "The Permian Extinction: *National Geographic* Comes Close to the Truth," Answers in Genesis, http://www.answersingenesis.org/tj/v15/i1/permian. asp.

4:19   Mike Oard, "The Extinction of the Dinosaurs," Answers in Genesis, http://www. answersingenesis.org/tj/v11/i2/dinosaur.asp.

4:20   Ken Ham, ed., *The New Answers Book* (Green Forest, Arkansas: Master Books, 2006), pp. 186–197.

Chapter 5: The Origin of Life

Article # Reference

5:1   David Demick, "Life from Life . . . or Not?" http://www.answersingenesis.org/ creation/v23/i1/life.asp.

5:2   Graham Cairns-Smith, *Genetic Takeover: And the Mineral Origins of Life*, (Cambridge: Cambridge University Press, 1982), quoted at http://www. answersingenesis.org/home/area/tools/Quotes/cairns-smith_RNA.asp.

5:3   Ken Ham, ed., *The New Answers Book 2* (Green Forest, Arkansas: Master Books, 2008), pp. 15–24.

Article #   Reference

5:4   Danny Faulkner, "What Went Wrong at NASA?" Answers in Genesis, http://www.
       answersingenesis.org/articles/am/v3/n1/what-went-wrong-at-nasa.

5:5   Aw Swee-Eng, "The Origin of Life: A Critique of Current Scientific Models," Answers
       in Genesis, http://www.answersingenesis.org/home/area/magazines/tj/docs/
       tjv10n3_origin_life.pdf.

5:6   Answers in Genesis, "Could Monkeys Type the 23rd Psalm?" http://www.
       answersingenesis.org/home/area/tools/xnv2n3.asp.

Chapter 6: The Origin of Microorganisms

Article #   Reference

6:1   Mike Oard, "Supposed Eukaryotic Evolution Pushed Back One Billion Years,"
       Answers in Genesis, http://www.answersingenesis.org/tj/v15/i1/eukaryote.asp.

6:2   Answers in Genesis, "Ancient Organisms Stay the Same," http://www.
       answersingenesis.org/creation/v21/i3/news.asp.

6:3   Mike Oard, "'Snowball Earth'—A Problem for the Supposed Origin of
       Multicellular Animals," Answers in Genesis, http://www.answersingenesis.org/tj/
       v16/i1/snowball.asp.

6:4   Georgia Purdom, "Round and Round We Go—Proposed Evolutionary
       Relationships Among Archaea, Eubacteria, and Eukarya," http://www.
       answersingenesis.org/cec/docs/evolutionary-relationships.asp.

6:5   Rick Swindell, "Shining Light on the Evolution of Photosynthesis," Answers in
       Genesis, http://www.answersingenesis.org/tj/v17/i3/photosynthesis.asp.

6:6   Georgia Purdom, "'Non-evolution' of the Appearance of Mitochondria and Plastids
       in Eukaryotes—Challenges to Endosymbiotic Theory," Answers in Genesis, http://
       www.answersingenesis.org/cec/docs/endosymbiotic-theory.asp.

6:7   Brad Harrub, and Bert Thompson, "Evolutionary Theories on Gender and Sexual
       Reproduction," http://www.trueorigin.org/sex01.asp.

Chapter 7: The Origin of Plants

Article #   Reference

7:1   Emmett L. Williams et al., "Precambrian Pollen: A Response to Questions about
       Creationist Research," http://www.rae.org/pollen.html.

7:2   Alexander Williams, "Did Plants Evolve?" Answers in Genesis, http://www.
       answersingenesis.org/creation/v19/i4/plants.asp.

Article #   **Reference**

9:8   Kurt Wise, "Does This Evolutionary Claim Have Any Legs?" http://www. answersingenesis.org/docs2006/0421legs.asp.

9:9   Jerry Bergman, "The Evolution of Feathers: A Major Problem for Darwinism," Answer in Genesis, http://www.answersingenesis.org/tj/v17/i1/feathers.asp.

9:10   Answers in Genesis, "Tiny Bones—Giant Assumptions," http://www. answersingenesis.org/creation/v22/i3/focus.asp.

9:11   Ken Ham, ed., *The New Answers Book* (Green Forest, Arkansas: Master Books, 2006), pp. 141–148.

9:12   Robert Doolan, "The Echidna Enigma . . . And the Platypus Puzzle," Answers in Genesis, http://www.answersingenesis.org/creation/v18/i2/echidna.asp.

9:13   Stuart Burgess, "The Beauty of the Peacock Tail and the Problems with the Theory of Sexual Selection," Answers in Genesis, http://www.answersingenesis. org/tj/v15/i2/peacock.asp.

9:14   Mike Oard, *Frozen in Time*, (Green Forest, Arkansas: Master Books, 2004), pp. 53–60, http://www.answersingenesis.org/home/area/fit/chapter5.asp.

Chapter 10: The Origin of Humans

Article #   **Reference**

10:1   Ken Ham, ed., *The New Answers Book 2* (Green Forest, Arkansas: Master Books, 2008), pp. 35–45.

10:2   Rebecca Driver, "Australia's Aborigines . . . Did They See Dinosaurs?" Answers in Genesis, http://www.answersingenesis.org/creation/v21/i1/aborigines.asp.

10:3   Gary Parker, *Creation Facts of Life: How Real Science Reveals the Hand of God* (Green Forest, Arkansas: Master Books, 2006), pp. 174–186, http://www. answersingenesis.org/cec/docs/cfl-pdfs.asp.

10:4   David DeWitt, "Chimp-Human Hybridization: Two of a Kind or Two Different Kinds?" Answers in Genesis, http://www.answersingenesis.org/ docs2006/0531chimp.asp.

10:5   David DeWitt, "Chimp Genome Sequence Very Different from Man," Answers in Genesis, http://www.answersingenesis.org/go/dna-chimp.

10:6   Mike Oard, "Neandertal Man—The Changing Picture," Answers in Genesis, http://www.answersingenesis.org/creation/v25/i4/neandertal.asp.